CONCERNING
TEILHARD

CONCERNING TEILHARD

and Other Writings on
Science and Religion

Bernard Towers

Fellow of Jesus College
Cambridge

Collins

ST JAMES'S PLACE LONDON

1969

© Bernard Towers 1969
Printed in Great Britain
Collins Clear-Type Press
London and Glasgow

DEDICATION

To my teachers, pupils and colleagues, with thanks for all they have taught me, and apologies for all I have neglected to learn from them.

CONTENTS

CONTENTS

INTRODUCTION:
WHERE THREE ROADS MEET

The three roads of my title are science, philosophy and religion. One feels at once the need to define what one means—or rather what one does not mean—by each of these terms. But that is what the book is about, and in any case it would be quite absurd to try to put into a nutshell topics that already occupy all too many miles of shelf-space in libraries all over the world. Let me only say that, for all the ink that has been spilled on them, these topics are far from exhausted. Discussion of them was never, in fact, of greater importance than it is now for contemporary society. In view of the quite extraordinary physical and biological powers that rest with us today, neglect of the question could, in the quite near future, lead to the destruction of society and civilisation. Such a statement is no empty exaggeration. The responsibilities facing society—that is, facing people—are enormous.

Whatever distractions we may be tempted to seek, and be glad to find, in this rather phrenetic age, we most of us discover that from time to time we ask ourselves such questions as 'who am I, and what if anything am I here for?', or, 'if it be true, as some seem to think, that people are only "naked apes", has an ape (or any other feature of "nature") any relevance or significance, or is everything really just a mess?', or again, 'is death—my own death, the death of relations and friends, the death of people on motorways, in Vietnam, or Biafra, or in earthquakes—anything more than a mark of ultimate absurdity in a manifestly absurd life?' All these are questions that seem to bother a good many of my acquaintances, both young and old. They certainly bother me. A modern discussion of them must take serious account of each of the three roads. Pompous theologians (and they haven't all joined in the self-immolation of their death-of-God colleagues) who are wholly ignorant of science—and often enough not merely ignorant, but also unconcerned about the fact—are to me as pathetic as those modern priests of scientific materialism who boast about the total irrelevance to them, and the coming overthrow, of religion. Pathetic too is a particular kind of modern philosopher, a man who by rights should be, as his title suggests, a 'lover of wisdom', but who spends his life in dotting logical i's and crossing linguistic t's, utterly divorced from the real problems that people have to face.

But let me say at once that I know of no place or system where the three roads do actually meet as part of human experience. One proceeds by approximations, and often enough by trying to clarify what a proposition is not, rather than what it is. If a pattern and meaning is to be discovered in our world-in-evolution it might be that, like the personal history of each one of us, it could be represented in a visual image or analogy as two cones standing upright base to base. As individuals we each start off as a point object—or at least a very small object, which of course also has a history that links it with that of the rest of the world. As individuals we grow, expand, explore and mature, and the lower cone takes shape. In an age of specialisation we may tend to develop more in one direction than in others. The resulting imbalance can be readily corrected, if only we recognise the value of other people's growth-patterns, and if we try to maintain our relations with others in some kind of social equilibrium. When our lives have reached about their half-way stage, according to Jung and other psychotherapists, what I am calling the upper cone begins to take shape. The individual begins to draw together, if circumstances are favourable, all the experiences of the earlier, divergent phase. We none of us ever reach, in life, quite as far as the apex of the upper cone, which is where all our particular roads of experience finally meet. That is our personal summation, or consummation, that is achieved only at death, if then. Perhaps it is the same with the world, which surely has a very long way to go yet, before its growth and development, its evolution, will bring it anywhere near its summit. In some respects the world appears still, only too obviously, to be in its divergent, divisive phase. But there are many signs that things are on the move. In science, for instance, as J. D. Bernal noted in his latest book, there is a 'convergent, generalising trend that is replacing the divergent and specialising trend of the nineteenth century with its various subjects separated by thought-proof partitions'.[1] It is not without time, and those diehards who currently exercise so much control must not be allowed to halt this process, or to hinder it unduly. The risk is too great: we now have the knowledge and the power actually to stop the world's development and destroy all living things if we so decide. So too, in terms of our individual development, we each have a personal option to suicide. Whatever we do or do not do, some change is inevitable. In seeking to bring it about ourselves we can be destructive and divisive if we so choose. But on the other hand we can each of us try, in however small a way, to bring the point of cosmic convergence a little nearer. And that is what this book is about.

There is no pretence or self-delusion, therefore, that one has actually arrived at the place where the three roads meet. It is all a question, really, of walking from time to time round the circumference of one's own converging cone, and of trying to see its meaning in relation to the larger one of which it forms a part. One walks some distance along each of the roads as one

1. Bernal, J. D., *The Origin of Life*, Weidenfeld and Nicolson, London, 1967, p. 159.

comes across them in turn, in the hope of getting a little nearer the summit. Sometimes one goes down instead of up. This seems to happen more particularly when one becomes so fascinated by and involved in one particular bit of road that one stays too long and begins to forget that the really important journey must involve some rough walking between one region and another. It is too easy to lose sight of the fact that the other roads are even there: after all, in the analogy we are pursuing, they are on the circumference of the circle, and each of the three is equidistant from its neighbour in either direction. On a circle, that means out of sight.

This could all be a specious plea in defence of superficiality. We are all so conditioned to the advantages won by late nineteenth-century specialism and the habit of compartmentalising knowledge, that anyone who does try to walk across rough ground, or to construct bridges between the specialist ways, runs the evident risk of being dubbed a dilettante. It may be all right for a professional journalist to try it, because his job is so to report on things that a mass-audience will understand or will think it understands. But for an academic it can spell death. Despite all the lip-service paid these days by educationalists to the need for interdisciplinary studies, woe betide anyone in the universities who has the temerity to take the challenge seriously. He makes himself into an Aunt Sally for his specialist colleagues, and the brickbats come thick and fast. The only sensible thing to do is to wear appropriate protective armour, in the shape of other publications of a more narrowly professional kind, and then rely on their good repute (and the 'respectable' appointments they produce) to get a hearing for one's wider interests. There will be some who will certainly decry the range of subjects covered in this book and my way of handling them—I am thinking especially of my fellow-scientists. But there may also be some who do not instinctively deplore the idea of breadth in thinking and writing. Broad streams, it is true, are often shallow ones. But on occasion they run deeper than the swift narrows.

Why just three roads for the title, though, and not thirty-three or ten times that number? There is certainly room, around my cones, for an indefinite number of roads. For one thing, in reply, it seems broadly true that all knowledge, all experience, can be included under one or other of these major categories, either science (at least in the broad sense), or philosophy or religion. But there is also for me a special significance in this particular analogy of three roads. As a boy, cycling or walking in the Pennines or the Lake District, I was often struck by the difference in what one can only call 'atmosphere' between, for instance, a crossroads (where four roads meet) and the place of my title. One cannot fail to notice the latter, nor can one fail to make some decision about it. With crossroads it is possible to go across or 'through' them, and never even be aware of the fact. I see this happening all the time in academic life, where people are usually so busy pedalling, with heads well down, that they never see anything much except the bit of road just in front of them, or even nothing but a bit of the machine that they happen to be riding. In some academic communities, of course, such as a Cambridge college, the system is geared to prevent, theoretically, the onset of academic myopia of the sort just referred to. But in many places the disease is endemic and seriously incapacitating.

Now if this is the way one is accustomed to riding one's bicycle, and if instead of a crossroads one comes to a place where three roads meet, one is bound to come a cropper. Such a place was always, to me, potentially exciting, especially if there was no signpost and one had to decide, up in the hills and miles from anywhere, whether it would be better to bear left or right, or to go back the way one had come. One had to live with one's mistakes, of course, even if it meant an extra twenty miles on one's cycle-ride. The idea of at any rate looking for a comparable situation in the world of thought has always had a powerful attraction for me. And even when one concludes that the 'goal' is literally out of sight and is bound to remain so for the time being, yet one's interest in exploring the approaches is a very keen one.

It is important not to muddle up the roads, or pretend they are really all the same one. What is called the 'concordist' theory of truth is to be sharply distinguished from the 'coherence' theory, which is one which I try systematically to follow. If I were given the choice (though perish the thought) between 'concordism' and the opposite view, namely, that major disciplines or fields of study have nothing relevant to offer each other, I would prefer the latter: because at least then, provided each separate road is followed honestly and straight, it is bound, in my view and on the double cone analogy, eventually to draw nearer to the others. Dialogue between them will become not only possible but eventually inescapable. It is then that one has to aim for 'coherence'. In the concordist approach—and let it be clear that concordism is not the pre-rogative of kindly but woolly-minded christians who desperately want to incorporate scientific findings into their statements of belief, but is also the approach of the self-styled 'progressives', whose 'scientism' is merely 'secular concordism', and subject to all the criticisms levelled at its ecclesiastical counterpart—in the concordist approach, in place of clarity and coherence, there is muddle all the way. A curious specialist language is developed and, as with all specialist, non-interacting groups, no dialogue but only monologue is finally possible, because nobody outside the group ever knows quite what is being said. Failure to communicate means isolation and, if it remains unchecked, spells eventual madness. There is and always must be a state of tension between science, philosophy and religion. Complacency (which denies tension) in these questions is always suspect. So too is triumphalism (which also denies tension) from whichever direction it comes—and scientific triumphalists sometimes shout louder these days than their ecclesiastical forerunners ever did. Tension is a measure of force, a measure of vitality. Those who feel no *Angst* are dead before their time.

There is another reason for my choice of three. A place where three roads meet is traditionally a dangerous one. I vividly remember the intensity of the visual image produced in me as a schoolboy in the classical sixth, when I read the line in the *Oedipus Rex* by Sophocles which simply states that it was at such a place that King Oedipus had, many years before, killed his father in a quarrel, not knowing who the man was. Long before I took any serious interest in Freud, it had seemed to me psychologically right that this was where the tragedy of Oedipus really began to take shape. Of course, in the play itself, one doesn't discover just where and how it happened until half way through the action, by which time its psychological impact is all that much greater. It will be remembered that, because of an oracle that he would kill his father and marry his mother, Oedipus had been exposed to die as an infant by his parents, King Laius and Queen Jocasta. Being rescued, and brought up, by foster-parents as their own son, Oedipus grew to manhood, when he heard a rumour about the terrible fate that might befall him. In order to escape it he fled to another country, which of course turned out to be that of his birth, where his tragedy was acted out as had been prophesied. This introductory chapter is no place for yet another interpretation of the Oedipus myth, nor, at one remove, for an interpretation of that 'complex' to which it has given rise in this century. But in the context of this essay one might perhaps draw a moral. In recent times science has been a veritable Oedipus, engaged in slaying (whether consciously or unconsciously is a matter for debate) its father-figure, theology. Now philosophy is the mother of science, having given birth to it, in western Europe, in the fourteenth century. A few decades ago philosophy, in its twentieth-century form known as logical positivism, was ready to play the part of Jocasta and to effect an unlawful union, which we know as scientific positivism.

It is as difficult to say who or what has been to blame in this modern tragedy, as it is to say who or what was to blame in the original Oedipus myth. Modern psychoanalysts, who only see part of the story, seem these days to point the finger at Jocasta, the mother-wife. But Laius the father must surely take some share of the blame, because he was too inflexible, and too concerned for his own safety and his own power. Again, in the original version of the story Oedipus was not so much sinned against as sinning, a man of *hubris*, headstrong and proud. Modern science is not unlike that. It may be that it has a similar nemesis awaiting it, as disillusionment creeps in amongst the public, and the call for vengeance begins to be heard, especially from the young. Oedipus certainly had to accept responsibility for his actions, according to Sophocles at least. Modern emasculated versions of the myth tend to take the blame off him and lay it on a supposedly domineering and possessive mother, which Jocasta in fact was not. The subject provides endless scope for reflection and comment, as all good myths do. We might just conclude that in all real tragedy, as in all real life, the truth is a mixture. Good and bad, guilt and suffering, virtue and happiness, all are ingredients that go into the composition of every character in the drama. If this book has any merit, it might help to indicate a way towards a viable reconciliation, and a way forward for contemporary man. One need not necessarily have to accept the psychoanalysts' view that it is essential to go right back to the beginning in order to resolve conflict. It may be enough, at least as a start, to work together in mutual tolerance and respect.

The chapters that follow comprise essays and reviews

written over a span of more than a decade. Many of them were originally given in the form of papers at meetings of one kind or another. As an experiment I sometimes gave the same paper to audiences of very different composition. The essays were often modified subsequently in the light of the discussion they provoked and also in the light of my own unending criticism of them. In preparing them for publication in book form I have done a certain amount of rewriting, but I have been careful not to introduce later ideas into earlier essays. Occasional repetition of ideas or of particular quotations has been eliminated except where the argument, with deeper analysis, seemed to warrant retention, or the quotation was good enough to bear repetition.

I feel no particular urge to apologise for presenting a book of essays rather than the 'sustained piece of writing' (often patently bogus) that contemporary fashion prefers. I do not accept the modern view that what is latest in composition is necessarily the most interesting, the most important or the most significant. Although I hope that this collection illustrates a certain development of thought, it is always quite possible for a wrong turning, or a succession of them, to lead one away from an earlier, and entirely valid, insight: after all one is sometimes struck, for instance, by the clarity with which quite a small child can grasp the essentials of an honest position, and can see through all the rationalisations and psychological projections with which, in later life, we sometimes try to hide our doubts and hesitancies.

It is, to me, one of the more extraordinary features of contemporary society, how many there are who welcome change in the environment and yet refuse to accept it within themselves. The sense of personal identity, and its continuity, is clearly behind the apparent need to deny that one *is* changing with the years, that one is growing old and will one day approach decay. The wish to deny facts such as these is seen at

its most absurd in the frantic effort of modern man to circum-
vent the ravages of time, to postpone death as long as possible,
and even to hope to abolish it. Many people seem to want to
pretend that death will not come, at any rate not to them.
Now the only way to incorporate into one's personality a
truth that one finds 'morbid', or difficult at first to accept, is to
accustom oneself to live with it constantly in order to get it
into proper perspective. I count myself fortunate in that my
profession as anatomist keeps the reality of death constantly
before my eyes, in post-mortem and dissecting rooms. It has
also given me what I regard as the clearest insight of my experience, namely, that just underneath the small differences we
see in people, differences in looks, in colour, height, weight,
even sex, there is an enormous range of 'being' wherein we
are all virtually indistinguishable from one another. No good
anatomist can be racialist in politics, or can think that there is
any fundamental importance to be attached to the distinctions
we commonly make on grounds of class or creed, money,
honours, and social position. Like beauty, differences are
present primarily in the eye of the beholder. They are also, for
the most part, quite literally only skin-deep. They are not to
be ignored, indeed, but they should be put into proper perspective. To an anatomist, death is a great leveller.

Ideas such as these are worked out in more detail later in the
book. Other chapters deal with various aspects of education,
and the relevance of history. Some are more narrowly philosophical. The first paper, chronologically speaking, on 'Science
and the Philosophy of Nature', (Section Two, Chapter 2,
pp. 148-58), was given to the Cambridge University Aquinas
Society shortly after I moved here. At the time I had not
realised just how flexible and open that discussion-group is,
and the treatment was more static and stereotyped than it
might have been. My gratitude to that distinguished society
for many valuable discussions over the years was never greater,

perhaps, than for its invitation in 1956 to a research-astronomer to read a paper on the cosmology (or rather 'cosmogenesis' as one now says) of Teilhard de Chardin. Previous to that meeting I had known of Teilhard only through my professional studies of human evolution, particularly with regard to his work with Davidson Black on fossil man in China. The speaker had had access in Belgium, during a long period, to a good many of the then unpublished writings of Teilhard. The account he gave of these far-reaching hypotheses on evolution appealed strongly to me, and I set about collecting what material I then could from the continent of Europe. My first published essay on Teilhard dates from 1958. It is reprinted, together with later ones, in this volume.

My own subsequent thinking has clearly been much influenced by Teilhard: not so much shaped perhaps (if that is not too immodest a thing to say), as enormously deepened. I find myself less irritated by some of the highly emotional attacks on Teilhard that have appeared, than by some of the equally emotional advocacy of some of his devotees. Time, and a certain balance of approach, are needed for a proper estimate of a pioneer thinker like Teilhard. I should like here to express my appreciation to Sir Peter Medawar, in memory of the afternoon we spent together in a BBC studio early in 1960 debating the significance of Teilhard for the Third Programme. The fact that he subsequently published what he did, and that I replied to his attack in a broadcast talk (reprinted in this collection), did not put paid to our friendship, and for this courtesy, which is often but not always to be found amongst scientists who disagree, I am grateful.

It is fashionable amongst some writers within our own scientific establishment (and of course Medawar's well-known onslaught has influenced them a great deal) to dismiss Teilhard as beneath contempt. Thus John Ziman, in his recent and important book, which makes a considerable advance on the kind of scientific positivism criticised above, curtly says, 'Let us have no truck with the mystical ineffabilities of the Teilhard de Chardin ilk.'[2] Such a statement illustrates a depth of ignorance about Teilhard, and a degree of insensitivity, which is all too prevalent amongst my 'hard-headed' scientific colleagues. Genuine pioneers are always vilified by some established figures. Although whatever is sound and important in the new ideas always wins through in the end, a campaign of abuse by men with influence always holds up the process. Whatever may happen to Teilhard's personal reputation (and he once said that he wanted no more than to be part of the foundations of a new 'building of earth') we cannot afford to neglect the understanding that he makes possible. It is becoming increasingly clear that we have no time to lose if science is to safeguard its own future and that of the civilisation to which it has contributed so much. It is partly because of my conviction that Teilhard has something to offer which is of quite crucial importance and significance, as we approach the twenty-first century, that I have drawn up this selection of writings. Not that they all deal with specifically Teilhardian themes, or use Teilhardian language. Most of the chapters came to be written only because I was invited to contribute a paper, article or review on a particular theme for a particular purpose. The connecting-link is inevitably my reflection on personal experiences, and I would simply include exposure to Teilhard's thought as one important experience amongst many. Nevertheless, I hope that the book may help towards a more informed contemporary appraisal of Teilhard in some intellectual quarters in this country. His influence increases year by year, and despite the abuse that is sometimes levelled at him (or perhaps obviously because of it), he is clearly not someone that any educated person can afford to ignore. Time is no

2. Ziman, J., *Public Knowledge: the Social Dimension of Science*, Cambridge University Press, 1968.

longer on our side where the future is concerned. We would do well, it seems to me, to study carefully the ways of thought of a man who, more than any other in this century, has grappled with the conflicts that are inherent in modern society.

1968.   *Jesus College,*
Cambridge

SECTION ONE

THE AREA OF CONFLICT AND TEILHARD'S APPROACH TO A SOLUTION

I

MAN IN MODERN SCIENCE

A paper read to the Newman Association, 1962

When I was invited to make this contribution to the series entitled 'The Conscience of the Sixties', it was suggested that I might pose two problems: (1) 'to what extent, in the light of recent achievements in the biological and medical sciences, is it legitimate to look on Man as a "mechanism"?' (the noun is usually qualified, of course, by the adjective 'mere'), and (2) 'To what extent do modern scientists, and particularly medical scientists, actually treat, and treat of, human beings as if they were "mere" machines?' Now since I am not, these days, engaged in medical practice, and no longer deal daily with people as patients; and since my contacts with my colleagues who are physicians in this sense have become more and more remote during my years of work in the academic world of pre-clinical science, I feel quite unfitted to carry out a survey of the clinical field in order to answer the second of the two questions.

But in so far as it has been advances in the so-called basic medical sciences of anatomy, physiology, biochemistry, pathology, genetics, etc., which have laid the basis for the unquestionably general view of the 'sixties' that Man *is* essentially a highly-complex arrangement of matter such as would justify the epithet 'living machine', it might be that a paper on Man as the anatomist sees him, combined with some philosophical reflections on the implications of the findings of my branch of modern science, might be helpful in the long run in trying to

25

get clear what a scientist is referring to when he talks about 'Man'.

Let me say, however, encroaching at once on the clinical field in which I have already disclaimed any real competence, that I can see no limit to, and would not want to see any limit placed on, the extent to which the application of modern biological techniques to the treatment of patients might be developed. The ethical questions are sometimes grave indeed. But once it has been established that it is ethically right to alleviate the sufferings or the malaise of a patient, and provided that the treatment as planned involves no element of injustice either to the patient himself or to others that may be involved, then the only proper and sensible approach is to make use of whatever technical procedures might be known to be efficacious, or to devise new ones for which there is a reasonable chance of success.

It is clear, for instance, that we are now in the early stages of tremendous technical developments in what has been called 'spare-part surgery'. The principle was established with the development of blood transfusion. By giving his blood anyone can, at slight and temporary cost to himself, help to save the life of another. Even whole-organ transplants are now feasible. Such operations are being performed, at specially equipped hospitals, in increasing numbers. Theoretically there is likely to be no limit to the extent to which these complicated and ingenious techniques might be developed. We may look now with composure on the transfer of blood from one individual to another—although it was only very recently that the collection of blood from one of Her Majesty's prisons evoked the response from a mother that she 'would rather see her child die than know that the blood of a criminal was circulating in her veins'. But what are we to say about the patient who has no functional kidneys of his own, who ought by rights to be dead, except that his body now contains someone else's kidney to do what his own could not? There is no reason to suppose that it will not in the near future be possible to replace a failing heart with a 'good' one from someone recently dead, or even from an animal of convenient size.[1] Reports seep through the Iron Curtain about certain types of investigations into the transplantation of nervous tissue. What would we say of the condition of a man who functions with the brain of another individual? Presumably his memories, and other processes of intellection, would in part at least be those of another. One can almost hear the anxious murmur, 'but what about the soul?' And indeed it is about 'the soul' that I want to reflect in this paper.

Theologians might object that a scientist has no right to talk about 'the soul', since this is a spiritual substance which is outside the realms of his enquiry. There is today, I fancy, an altogether too facile distinction made, as a result of the ever-increasing specialisation of subjects of study, between the realms that are proper to the scientist, those proper to the philosopher, and those reserved for the theologian. It is of course convenient to classify and sub-divide subjects of study, and there is much to be said for cobblers sticking to their lasts. At least it allows each to develop ideas in his subject in comparative freedom from the attacks of the ill-informed! But when you are dealing with concepts about the nature of Man, such an approach only emphasises those ever-deepening divides which effectively prevent communication between different groups of specialists. We cannot afford to allow a specious plea on behalf of specialism to cloak what sometimes

1. This was written in 1962, as the chapter-heading indicates. The period of over five years that elapsed before the subject of heart-transplants became 'news' was rather longer than one had thought would be the case, and it is clear that even now (1968) there are many technical problems remaining.
Readers are requested, when they come across words like 'recently' in this book, to note the date of composition, which is always indicated at the beginning or end of the chapter concerned.

amounts to real ignorance about and lack of feeling for whole ranges of knowledge about human beings. The lip-service paid by some theologians to the activities of scientists, and vice versa, is not enough. One must somehow become 'involved', and real involvement requires experience that goes far beyond a second-hand reading about a subject. While it is important that one should not so blur the edges of recognisable disciplines that they lose all effective 'discipline', yet it is essential, for Man to be fully human, that he should integrate and synthesise experience of all kinds so as to produce a meaningful account of his own existence.

The problems posed by the confrontation of two or more disciplines are enormous indeed. It is easy to see why so many prefer to bury their heads in the sands, or the rock, of their own specialism. But it is this very intellectual effort, painful and full of anguish though it may be, that is required, it seems to me, by the 'Conscience of the Sixties'. It is no longer good advice simply to be good and let who will be clever. The pace of technological advance, whether in the sciences of life or in those of destruction and death, is so rapid, that without a great many 'agonising re-appraisals' we shall lose our grip on all those civilising coherences that have been built up so slowly during the last few thousand years.

The scientific method can be applied to the study of Man under either of two quite distinct aspects. The first is that which we have already touched upon, to take Man as he manifests himself in full maturity. That is, to study you and me as adult, living, functioning, thinking biological organisms. Such a study is subdivided by the biological scientist into anatomy (the study of structure), physiology and biochemistry (the study of the laws which govern the interaction of the thousands of structural components of the body), and psychology (the study of causes and effects in the sphere of mental activities). The second aspect under which Man is studied by the scientist is that of development, and this is in fact the line I want to follow here. Development is to be understood to comprise two aspects of study, ontogeny and phylogeny, the development of the individual man as child of his parents, and the evolutionary development of the species *Homo sapiens*.

My reasons for choosing to discuss the development of Man rather than the finished product, with reference to the problem of 'the soul', are threefold: firstly, because I am myself a student of embryology and evolution, and I am often asked such questions as, 'when is the soul infused into the embryo?' and 'granted the truth of the general theory of evolution, at what point did Man receive his soul?'; secondly, because it seems to me that it is only through the study of developmental or historical processes that one ever begins to understand anything; and thirdly, as a corollary to the second point, it seems to me to be not only illogical to plunge *in medias res* in an attempt to define one's subject of study, but positively dangerous when one's subject is Man: because one can hardly help, in such an approach to Man, to refer constantly to one's most immediately available specimen, oneself. *Cogito, ergo sum.* It is the introspection of Descartes, combined with his adoption of the Baconian myth that it is possible to be wholly objective in one's analysis of 'things' (looked at as 'machines') outside oneself, that is symptomatic of the endemic schizophrenia of Western civilisation. People suffering from this 'disease' present themselves in one of three forms: first the materialist monist, who says all things are machines, himself included; second the dualist, for whom the human machine lodges a ghost which is the real man; and thirdly the idealist, for whom there really *are* only ghosts.

The modern scientist who restricts his enquiry to adult human beings almost forces himself to become either a monist like his great classical predecessor Democritus, or a dualist like Plato. Thinking of the soul as a ghost in the machine has been a constant temptation to all christians. A great deal of spiritual writing, as of philosophical and theological writing, seems simply to assume a thorough-going dualism of body and soul, as if these were two 'things' in the same logical category, temporarily united on earth but separated at death to the great benefit (it is often implied) and 'relief' of soul. Clearly it is possible to hold some such view and remain within the Church. But whenever such dualism of body and soul, matter and spirit, has been taken to its logical conclusions, as with the Manichees, Albigensians, Jansenists and Puritans—and there are many about today—it has been formally condemned as heretical. The Church's opposition to even moderate forms of dualism stems ultimately from the biblical view of Man, which always considers him 'in the flesh', and does not distinguish between his 'soul' on the one hand, and his 'anima', 'psyche' or 'life', on the other.

A scientist who is a philosophical dualist—and there are many who are—is faced with the problem of how and where the soul interacts with the body. The point of interaction is no longer placed, it is true, where Descartes put it, in the pineal gland. Professor Eccles, the distinguished neurophysiologist, for whom the soul is the seat of intellection and free-will, would place the point somewhere in the synapses between nerve-cells in the cerebral cortex. Professor Penfield would put it somewhere in the reticular substance of the brain-stem, about three inches behind and between the eyes. This is a region long thought of as significant when one gazes into a person's eyes, those 'windows of the soul', as they have been called. It feels as if one is looking straight at the 'real person', who is 'situated' inside the skull.

The growth of psychology in recent years has made us realise to what a remarkable extent our psychological activity is affected by changes in the physical organism, by alterations, including of course disease-processes, in the 'machine'. Christian psychologists affected by that dualistic philosophy which runs an unbroken course, in Western Europe, from Plato through Descartes to the present day, have wanted to distinguish between the 'psyche' of man, as no more than one aspect of his physical makeup, a part of the machine dependent on correct working of all the other parts, and his 'soul' which, being a spirit, remains unaffected by physical or psychological changes in his body. These views were ably contradicted in Victor White's *Soul and Psyche*.[2] However much we may be tempted to relieve ourselves of difficult problems by making distinctions between the 'life of the body' and the 'life of the soul', we must remember, with Father Victor White, that 'the soul is that *whereby* we live'. It is through the activity of the soul that we live and move and have our being, whether we are simply enjoying a good meal or using the strength the food gives us to think uplifting thoughts.

It is said that men can be divided into Platonists and Aristotelians. I am in the latter group. I cannot make sense of the dualist position, and recent advances in developmental biology seem to me to make Platonism in this sense virtually untenable. To an Aristotelian, the soul is 'the form of the body', that principle of organisation which makes any *thing* into *what* it is. The soul of a man is firstly, then, that organised coherence of matter *whereby* he lives, the organisation which makes him *what* he is, which makes him indeed, not just 'man', but which makes him Tom or Dick or Harry. But man is unique in another sense as well. Unlike the 'forms' or 'souls' of all other earthly creatures, the soul of man is capable of transcending the limitations inherent in any 'principle of physical organisation': on those relatively rare occasions when we really *think*, or when we pray, or when we freely choose, it is the same soul operating as in all other activities. But, however much we may have been conditioned by processes explicable in bio-

2. White, Victor, *Soul and Psyche*, Collins and Harvill Press, London, 1960.

logical terms, when we do these things we go beyond what is *biologically* conceivable. It is not the 'soul' that thinks or prays or chooses, it is the whole man. It is the man who is the spiritual being, not a ghost in a temporary prison. True we have to say that in some way the spirit, having transcendental qualities, survives the death, the breakdown of the organisation, of the biological organism through which it manifests itself on earth. But such a death, and such a curious form of survival, is not man's final destiny: he is destined for the resurrection of the body, and thereafter he will enjoy or suffer eternal life precisely as Tom or Dick or Harry. There is no place in the christian view of eternal life for ghosts permanently liberated from their machines. It is the whole man that survives, 'warts and all'.

If this is the right view of the 'body-soul relationship', then any living creature which possesses the organising principle characteristic of a human being is, by definition, informed by a human soul. And here we come to the question of the soul of the developing embryo. Theological opinion today seems overwhelmingly to be in favour of the theory of 'Immediate Animation' of the human embryo. This theory states that the embryo is informed by a fully human soul 'from the moment of conception', as it is usually expressed. The phrase itself ignores the fact that conception is not an event but a process: it takes at least half an hour between the time that the successful spermatozoon begins to penetrate the ovum and the final fusion of the two pro-nuclei of the cell. There are other difficulties too about the theory of 'Immediate Animation', to which we shall return later. St Thomas Aquinas, who followed Aristotle in these matters, held instead the theory of 'Mediate Animation'. He taught that the developing human being *in utero* was 'informed' by a succession of souls, vegetative, animal and subsequently human. For St Thomas a male embryo became human at approximately 40 days of development, but a female embryo not until 80 days. These views, when heard by people who are confused between Aristotelian and Platonic views on the nature of the soul, have given rise to much confusion, and indeed to ribaldry when it is remembered that Western Europe has for a long time been a patriarchal society. In fact, however, it seems to me that the theory represents a perfectly straightforward descriptive account of human embryological development. The ancients could not have *guessed* these things, even to the business of 40 and 80 days. Careful studies must have been made, by Aristotle and others, on the products of human conception, in abortions whether spontaneous or procured, at all stages of development. With the naked eye all that one sees during the first twenty days after conception is the partially-coagulated blood surrounding an 'ovum' which looks like a sea-anemone with its frond-like processes. The actual embryo inside cannot be recognised, unless one has a magnifying lens and knows just what to look for and where. To describe this as a vegetative stage of development is reasonable enough. As the actual embryo becomes big enough to see, it first looks very like any other vertebrate embryo. It is not so long ago since Haeckel was so impressed with the similarities that he said all embryos, of whatever species, were identical. We know now that this is not so, but at first sight it looks like it. To call this an 'animal stage of development', again is reasonable enough. Aristotle's 'forms' (vegetative, animal, human) are, after all really classificatory concepts. In modern embryology we speak of the human embryo becoming a fetus when it acquires recognisable human form. [*Note:* My reasons for using this 'American' spelling were explained in the following note published in the BMA's journal, *Archives of Disease in Childhood*, in April 1967: Cambridge students who have attended my Embryology classes during the past decade will know (if they remember) that our American colleagues are correct (though perhaps unwittingly so) in their spelling of the word *fetus*. One recognises that language is like a living organism, and undergoes evolutionary change. We would, however, be reluctant to abandon our own *paediatrics*, *gynaecology*, or *orthopaedics*. But there is nothing, except the always interesting 'history of errors', to recommend the traditional English and French *foetus*.

Classical Latin authors had a word for what a mother brought to birth: it was unquestionably *fetus*. The putative root is *fe-*, from *feo*, *fere* (to bear), which has given us a host of splendid words such as *female*, *fecund*, *felicitude*—and also, it may be noted, *effete*, for one who has ceased producing offspring.

Fetus was the only spelling in use up to the year 600 A.D.[3] No originality is claimed for the observation that the new spelling was introduced by Isidorus (c. 560-636 A.D.), who was Archbishop of Seville, and one of the most influential figures in the Dark Ages. His literary output was prodigious.[4] His learning, though considerable, was not really adequate to his purpose, and much that he wrote in, for instance, his twenty-volumed 'Etymologies' was erroneous, partly because, as has been noted,[5] his Latin was 'not pure'. For all his errors, though, he was one of the few who kept alive some semblance of classical learning at a time matched only by our own for general indifference and insensitivity to history.[6]

Isidorus appears to have been misled by the Greek word *ΦΟΙΤΌΣ*, itself a later corruption of *ΦΥΤΌΣ*, a word meaning 'fertile'. *The Shorter Oxford Dictionary* (3rd edition 1947) gives only the spelling *foetus*, and says that 'the better form with

3. Souter, A., *Glossary of Later Latin*, Oxford, 1949.
4. *Encyclopaedia Britannica*, 11th edition, Cambridge, 1910.
5. Wace, F., and Percy, W. C., *Dictionary of Christian Biography and Literature*, London, 1911.
6. Towers, B., 'Medical Scientists and the View that History is Bunk', *Persp. Biol. Med.*, 1966, 10, pp. 44-55. Reprinted here as Chapter 8 of Section Two.

e is almost unknown in use'. But Partridge[7] states the true facts quite bluntly, in a way that should give pause to authors and editors alike.

It would be a gesture towards Anglo-American *entente* if Western Europe were to abandon an error that has persisted for over 1300 years. Perhaps in return our American colleagues would leave their word *pediatrics* to the footmen, where it could conceivably, though still incorrectly, belong.

As to plurals, the correct form is *fetūs* with the long second syllable (never, of course, *feti*, from the sight and sound of which both mind and heart recoil). But perhaps it would be altogether too pedantic to insist on such 'difficult' plurals these days, and I for one would settle for *fetuses*.] The nomenclature is arbitrary, of course, but the agreed stage for change of title is when the creature is about 3 centimetres long. This stage is reached towards the end of the seventh week. The dates agree pretty well with St Thomas, at any rate for males. Now sex-determination is done, with the naked eye, by examination of the external genital organs. Here I can do no better in substantiating ancient opinion than to quote from a standard textbook of embryology[8]: 'Up to approximately the 25 mm. stage (i.e. between 40 and 45 days—B.T.) the appearances of the external genitalia of the female resemble very closely those of the male . . . Wilson (1926), however, found that only after the 50 mm. stage (i.e. about 75 days—B.T.) could the sex be determined from external characters without error.' In other words, because of the early appearances of the 'phallic tubercle', every embryo looks more like a male until nearly 80 days, when the characteristic female form is assumed by those which

7. Partridge, E., *Origins: A Short Etymological Dictionary of Modern English*, London, 1958.
8. Hamilton, Boyd and Mossman, *Human Embryology*, 2nd ed., Heffer & Sons Ltd., Cambridge, 1952, p. 252.

actually are female. The ancients were not far out in their reckonings.

Of course, if we study the developing human embryo with modern techniques of microscopy, we know that it can properly be called 'human' right from the time of conception. The chromosomal pattern in the nucleus of the fertilised ovum, from which each individual develops, is specific to the human species. Indeed, the nucleus is specific to the individual man or woman to be, in so far as many of his or her future characteristics are there predetermined according to the laws of genetic inheritance: predetermined by the chemical configuration of the chromosomes themselves. Therefore every fertilised human ovum is literally unique, in that the genetic endowment of each individual is unique. The fertilised ovum contains all the genetic instructions, the principle of organisation or 'form' in the Aristotelian sense, that will cause it to develop precisely into Tom and not Harry. Even in the case of identical twins, where each has the same genetic endowment, it is probable that the twinning is itself genetically determined, so that this organisation, the instruction for twinning, was present in the original cell, making it potentially two. The analysis is more difficult with artificially induced identical twins. The technique is well-developed in lower vertebrates but not as yet in mammals.

The genetic endowment, conferring individuality on the developing organism, survives, in experimental animals, even the transfer of the embryo from the natural mother into the body of a foster mother. Techniques for such transplantations are already well developed in domestic animals, and there is no theoretical reason why they should not in due course be applied to human embryos. Transplantation at first would be into the body of a human foster mother, but ultimately perhaps into an artificial culture-medium. So far as one can tell there is no reason why fertilised ova cultured in this way

should not develop into entirely normal men and women with immortal souls like any of us.[9] Such a *Brave New World* picture gives rise, in many people, to feelings of horror and disgust. To me it appears as a logical extension of Man's increasing control over his environment, one to be welcomed or deplored, as are other human activities, according to the ethical motives and practice of those who utilise the techniques. But what it does seem to do is make nonsense of a popular, restricted notion of a transcendent Deity who is active in the 'creation' of individuals only in the sense of miraculously intervening for the 'infusion' or 'pouring in' of a soul. Such an idea makes sense only in the framework of a dualist interpretation of body-soul relationships which we expressly repudiate.

This, you may think, may be all very well for a pagan Aristotelian, or for a traducianist like Tertullian. Is Man's immortal soul inherited, like so much else, from his parents? Is the human soul 'educed' out of matter, as St Thomas says vegetative and animal souls are? Pius XII, in *Humani Generis*, allows for speculation about human evolution, but carefully confines speculation to the development of the human *body*. He goes on, 'that souls are immediately created by God is a view which the Catholic faith imposes on us.' We must ask what is meant by 'soul' and what is meant by 'created'. There are two matters of Faith involved here. One is the doctrine of the personal immortality of the individual man, which would seem to be placed in jeopardy if by soul we mean no more than a complex arrangement of matter which disintegrates with physical death. The second is the doctrine of a personal God who 'engraces' us, who cares for each one of us, personally and directly, throughout our lives. Is it possible to safeguard the

9. I refer here only to physical structure and spiritual potential, and not to fully developed 'persons'. Psychological development requires, of course, much more than simple physical nourishment.

theological doctrines within the framework of modern scientific knowledge about the development of Man?

I come now to consider briefly the question of the development in evolutionary time of the species *Homo sapiens*. It is important that we orientate ourselves properly here with regard to our concept of the passage of time; what constitutes a long time, and what constitutes a short time. The natural and normal time-yardstick for each one of us is the length of our own personal lifespan to date. Twenty years looks very different at the age of ten from what it does at sixty. Grandfathers seem both old and old-fashioned. So-called 'ancient history' deals with events some two to two-and-a-half thousand years ago. The history of Christendom itself seems long beyond imagining. It requires a very great mental effort indeed to think instead in terms of the passage of evolutionary time: thirty thousand years perhaps for evident proof of the existence of races of creatures that were indistinguishable from modern Man—certainly structurally indistinguishable, and probably mentally too, in terms at least of some sort of community life in the human sense and the development of skills and of art appreciation; up to sixty thousand years for the other known member of the genus *Homo*, namely Neanderthal Man.

The next largest taxonomic group, i.e. from the point of view of scientific classification, after the *genus* is the family, and today we must include in the Family *Hominidae* that group of fossils which some palaeontologists prefer to put together in a single genus known as *Pithecanthropus*. These creatures made tools and used fire, and they flourished about two hundred thousand years ago—that is, one hundred *times* the period since the 'ancient world' so-called. Another tool-making creature, *Zinjanthropus*, who flourished some *six* hundred thousand years ago, has recently been discovered in Tanganyika. And then we have that remarkable group from South Africa known collectively as the *Australopithecines*, upright plain-dwelling creatures, who lived perhaps a million years ago. And, still within the Family *Hominidae*, we are only, to the student of evolution, in what is called the 'Recent Period'. The order *Primata* goes back to the very beginning of the story of mammals as a whole, some sixty, seventy, with foreshadowings up to possibly a hundred or more million years ago. Words like 'beginning', or phrases like 'sudden appearance in the class Mammalia', are hopelessly misleading when the period of time concerned in an 'appearance' is of the order of millions, or, even for modern man say, of tens of thousands, of years.

In the nineteenth century it was readily assumed by some scientists that Man was a very recent offshoot from some ape-like stock, from gorilla, chimpanzee or orang-utan. The theory was convenient for those materialists who wanted to dethrone Man and reduce him to the level of 'the brutes'. It was convenient also for the theologian, who could point to the evident differences in the mental and spiritual qualities of man and the apes, and ascribe the differences to the 'infusion' of a rational, immortal soul. This view of Man as a recent descendant from ape-stock persists in some measure, in modern taxonomy, amongst those who would group the two families *Hominidae* and *Pongidae* as members of a super-family, the *Hominoidea*. But no knowledgeable scientist of today (as distinct both from his nineteenth-century predecessors and from the writers of popular books and newspaper articles on the subject of human evolution), would want to say that Man's immediate ancestors were anything like any of the modern species of ape. Disraeli is said to have asked himself the rhetorical question, in a debate in 1864, 'Is Man an ape or an angel?', and to have replied, with debating skill and little else, 'My lord, I am on the side of the angels.' A theologian could have told him, I hope, that he was wrong to think of man as a kind of angel *manqué*. A scientist today would be a good deal less dogmatic than Thomas Henry

Huxley used to be. There are palaeontologists who would want to say that the human stock separated out from common primate ancestors (which looked, perhaps, something like the gentle *tarsier* of today), as long ago as forty million years. The work of Professor Hürzeler on that curious primate of ten million years ago, *Oreopithecus*, may prove of crucial importance in this scientific debate. The curious thing about Man from the anatomical point of view (and *Oreopithecus* resembles him in this respect) is that he has retained so many of the *generalised* features of the primates, and has avoided many of the structural specialisations of modern apes. The old idea was that some group of tree-dwelling brachiating apes developed especially keen vision and manual dexterity as part of their mode of life. As a result they developed bigger brains, and eventually became clever enough to risk descent to the plains within the last few hundred thousand years. This view is often expounded even today in popular books and newspaper articles. But it is very suspect, and some scientists feel strongly enough about its errors as to say, as did Professor Straus in his closing remarks as chairman of a conference on 'The Nonhuman Primates and Human Evolution': 'The concept of a "chimpanzee" stage in human evolution is, to put it mildly, a bit atavistic—it is downright Haeckelism.'[10]

If one regards the human soul as a spiritual substance, separately created and 'infused' into the body at a moment in time, then philosophically and theologically, and abstracting all emotional considerations, there would seem to be no fundamental reason why one type of primate should have been chosen as recipient rather than another, or indeed why a vertebrate rather than invertebrate. A beetle, let us say, or a cow, might have been granted the privilege of receiving this newly-created spiritual substance. And yet it looks as though the history of human evolution is the story of a continuous

10. Straus, W. L. Jr., *Human Biology*, 1954, vol. 26.

development, in one particular group of primates, themselves a particular group of mammals which are a particular group of vertebrates, over a very, very long period of time. Specifically human development might have taken forty or fifty million years to accomplish, with other groups of primates such as the apes developing alongside, by what is known as parallel or possibly even convergent evolution. Biologically speaking, the structural and functional changes that have occurred over this period appear to have been, for the most part, individually imperceptible, and have become finally manifest, as it were, only in retrospect. Recent discoveries are steadily bridging the gaps between undoubtedly human and undoubtedly sub-human forms. If, as seems likely, it comes to be proved that there were no big jumps, and no breaks in the series, then some profound rethinking at the theological level will be required. Some of us think that the time has already come to make a start on the necessary rethinking. It may be that the phylo-genetic development of Man as a species is similar in many ways to that ontogenetic development of which some account has been given above. Just as each one of us constitutes an 'organism' so too, in some senses, does the species as a whole. Society is an organism. And, if the species is thus an integrated whole, so too, according to evolutionary theory, will be the genus, the family, the order, the class, the phylum, the animal kingdom and indeed the whole cosmos within which and from which living things have arisen.

The question now to be put is, 'how is our modern know-ledge about the development of Man to be interpreted in the light of christian teaching concerning God's personal involve-ment with each one of his human creatures?' And indeed, on the other side, 'how is christian teaching to be interpreted in the light of modern biological findings?'

For myself I can only think that answers to these questions, if and when they are devised, will be placed somewhere within the general framework of a Teilhardian synthesis. Teilhard de Chardin accepts that there is an essential distinction between Man and all other animals, but he extends the range of God's personal and immediate concern, as the Gospels do, beyond the individual man to include also the individual sparrow and the lily of the field. This is not to detract from the status of Man, but to elevate that of the rest of creation. Then we shall be able to sing again, as the psalmists did, of animals and birds, trees and shrubs, rocks and water joining together in praise of God. This is no return to a primitive animistic view of the world of nature, but is a straightforward statement of the latent powers of nature acting through the evolutionary process. Granted that with the advent of self-reflective Man a fundamentally new 'state' appeared, yet it was through so-called natural causes, I believe (that is, without the need for 'miracle', that is for a different *kind* of divine 'intervention'), that Man arose within and from a stock of pre-human living beings. Since the soul of Man is spiritual, and God is intimately and immediately concerned in its 'creation', the implication is that the 'souls' of other creatures also have spiritual, if not necessarily immortal, dimensions, and that God is 'involved' with them as well as with us.

The current, popular view of Man as a 'mere machine' stems from an over-concentration in the past on God's transcendence, and the consequent depersonalisation of nature. If nature is a 'mere machine', then so too will be Man, who is part of nature. The disrespect paid in the past to the things of nature is now made to include Man. The rescue-operation demanded by the 'Conscience of the Sixties' involves a rescue not only of Man the microcosm, but also of the macrocosm itself.

The Month, 1964, vol. 217, pp. 25-36.

2

TEILHARD AND THE PHENOMENON OF MAN

Le Phénomène Humain has been a best-seller in France since its posthumous publication in 1955. The initial impact of the translation, published as *The Phenomenon of Man*,[1] has been considerable. Never before, one imagines, in English publishing history, has a book by a Roman Catholic priest received such remarkable tributes in all types of journals and newspapers. 'Book of the year' for a number of well-known critics, 'possibly the book of the century' for one *Sunday Times* contributor.

During the period when Teilhard's works were available only in French, one had heard doubts expressed as to whether he would ever appeal to more than a few in this country. After the events of recent months there is now every indication that the Teilhardian movement will become as international in character as was Teilhard himself. It looks as if the influence of this remarkable man will come to be felt more and more in many different branches of human endeavour during the next few decades. For myself, I would go so far as to say that Teilhard's vision—he writes like a visionary, but a visionary whose feet are always planted very firmly on or in terra firma—marks the most significant achievement in synthesis since that of Aquinas. We cannot afford to neglect him because, quite simply, he seems in so many matters, and those the most important, to be so essentially right. His genius has sown many

1. Collins, London, 1959 (rev. ed. 1965).

seeds which, in so far as they fall on receptive and fertile ground, would seem destined to grow and flower according to the pattern of those same laws of development which lie at the heart of his system of thought.

The title of the first of the *Cahiers* to be published by L'Association des Amis de Pierre Teilhard de Chardin is, in its English form, *Building the Earth*. The articles all look to the future, being devoted to the subject which came to occupy Teilhard more and more in his later years. Much of his life was spent in the study of the far-distant past. But he became increasingly conscious that the patterns displayed throughout the course of evolutionary history are of the greatest significance if we are to appreciate what paths might be open to mankind in the future. The future of Man is a popular subject these days for speculative biologists. For some it represents a nice academic exercise. For Teilhard it was more than this. It is not a question for him just of working out correlations and probabilities on the basis of observations sufficient in number to ensure statistical accuracy. For Teilhard science, whether it be of the past or the present or, by extrapolation, of the future, is by no means the sort of donnish crossword puzzle that some of our contemporaries delight in. For the positivist and the relativist this is what, inevitably, science becomes. Clues are followed up and fruitful answers found, that is answers which will allow for or suggest the solution to other clues. But to ask, 'is this answer true?', or, 'what does this solution mean?', let alone, 'what does it all mean?' is, for many exponents of current scientific orthodoxy, to talk in a way which is neither meaningful nor useful. Does one ask what is the 'inner meaning' of a crossword puzzle? It is enough that it provides an intellectual pastime that is stimulating in the challenge and satisfying in the performance.

It is perhaps significant that of the distinguished Reith lecturers of recent years the two biologists (J. Z. Young and

P. B. Medawar)[2] might with justice be counted amongst the ablest exponents of this type of scientific, aseptic positivism. *Aseptic*, as many would see it, in the sense of being untainted with metaphysical questions about truth or value in any significant sense. This is a kind of speculation which, in the orthodox view, is to be ruled out as against the laws of the game, as being scientifically unverifiable in principle. *Aseptic*, as others would see it, in the sense of being at bottom sterile, destined finally to perish of inanition; a system which contains within itself the seeds of its own destruction, namely the inherent contradiction of the meaninglessness of meaning.

In this country and in America exponents of scientific positivism wield immense influence in the field of the biological sciences. Attempts to put other points of view are highly suspect in some professional circles. Now Teilhard speaks the language both of science and of theology. We know that some theologians are suspicious of him. What of scientists? In my opinion, if Teilhard's views are to be censured, the attack is more likely to come from some of the more orthodox members of the scientific hierarchy than from their counterparts in theology. Indeed, if Teilhard is right in his understanding of the process of evolution, then the writing is on the wall for scientific positivism. That system will not prevail if human evolution continues. No system will, of course, if the whole process is destined, by man's own folly, to be brought to an end. Such a cataclysm could only result from the exercise of that very freedom to produce it which man has acquired as the goal and purpose of the evolutionary process itself. But assuming survival of our present civilisation I think it unlikely that science will be able to progress if its only source of inspiration is positivism. Something of this sort was well expressed in

2. This was written in 1960. Since then other Reith lecturers from the biological sciences have included G. M. Carstairs and E. R. Leach. In each case their approach has been very different from the one here criticised.

a recent essay by R. A. Crowson the taxonomist in one of the Darwin celebration volumes.[3] The essay is entitled 'Darwin and Classification', and it concludes as follows:

> Unfortunately the advanced societies of today recognise only two motives for human endeavour—economic gain and pleasure; and if the pursuit of a natural classification is not to be justified in terms of economic gain, then modern men will insist that it must come under the category of pleasure. A hundred years ago a third type of motive was socially recognised—the pursuit of virtue and piety; and in the pre-Darwin and pre-Huxley age the justification of natural history was seen in these terms. The dedicated naturalist had something of the aura of a priest or monk, as the revealer of the divine mysteries of creation, and it would have seemed irreverent to suggest that anything that was worth God's while to create was not worth man's while to study. Whether systematic natural history can continue to flourish when its practitioners are looked on merely as a rather odd variety of pleasure-seekers remains to be seen.

It is more exciting to some people, of course, to engage in, say, experimental embryology than in taxonomy. But whatever may be the intrinsic interest of the particular field of study, if the scientist's motivation is restricted to economic gain and pleasure, his science is likely either to become corrupt or effete, finally to die from a shortage of practitioners of the proper quality. There will always be a few people, and those amongst the most gifted intellectually, who will be happy to spend their lives doing crossword puzzles, especially if there are worth-while prizes offered for correct solutions. But most people like to regard their work in terms more significant than this.

3. *A Century of Darwin*, ed. S. A. Barnett, Heinemann, London, 1958.

It is precisely to the real significance of modern scientific knowledge that Teilhard first and foremost brings the attention of his readers. The ability of man to understand, and not merely to know. Understanding implies the ability to distinguish between what is true and what is false, and the distinction is an unqualified one, even though the particular truth or falsity can be understood only in relation to others. Here Teilhard rejects entirely—though he does so always with abundant charity—the position of the positivist-evolutionist who would regard man's intellectual activities as no more than yet another evolutionary gimmick, a type of specialisation which has had great survival value for us up to now, but a specialisation which might well result, as is known to have happened with many examples of extreme specialisation during the course of evolution, in final extinction of the species. Teilhard would reply that the position of *Homo sapiens* is an altogether different case from that of specialised groups in former epochs as, for instance, in the age of ruling reptiles before the mammals entered into their inheritance. Man is unique precisely by virtue of his capacity for understanding. He not only knows, but knows that he knows. In Man we see the evolutionary process achieving its final significance. It does so by a process of turning in on itself, becoming conscious of itself. Man's knowledge is not limited to that derived from personal experience of the here and now, as is that of other living beings. His powers of understanding appear to know no bounds. He has unlimited capacity for acquiring and transmitting information and, more significantly, for assessing the quality of the information he receives, for accepting what is true and rejecting what is false. Teilhard insists on the reasonableness of the world. The world, of which we form a part, can be known and understood. Man can arrive at truths about it, if only by degrees and primarily by the use of the scientific method. Teilhard, as befits a great scientist, is a great champion of science and the scientific method, related as it always is to phenomena. Modern science is for him one of the most significant achievements of Man, an activity amongst the noblest available to us. The dust out of which we are literally fashioned is now observing, studying, and to some extent understanding itself. Living dust that can reflect upon itself and its history. The greatest single discovery of modern science is the fact of evolution, that process which stretches out through thousands of million years in the past, is always somewhere in action, and of which the end in time can in no way be foreseen. But what that end will be is, in Teilhard's view, now discernible. It will be when 'God shall be all in all' (1 Cor. 15, 28).

Teilhard understood St Paul's 'all' quite literally. His life was devoted, one might say, to the study of the implications of this text above all. He referred to it specifically in the last entry he made in his Diary on April 7th 1955, recently published as the last page of *L'Avenir de L'Homme*,[4] volume 5 of his collected works. In a sense this entry constitutes a summary of his faith and his life's work. Three days later, on Easter Sunday, he was quite suddenly, and in some ways most fittingly, taken from this world. He had once said that of all the days in the year he would best like to die on Easter Day. This hitherto obscure passage from St Paul acquired real meaning for Teilhard through his appreciation of the nature of the evolutionary process. This always seeks and always finally achieves increase in 'complexification' and hence increase in freedom. 'All' then includes the whole history of cosmogenesis up to the present and beyond, through inorganic barysphere and lithosphere, hydrosphere and atmosphere, to biosphere and noosphere, those successive 'layers' of the world. Each stage, inorganic, organic and mental represents a great increase in complexifica-

4. Subsequently published in English translation as *The Future of Man*, Collins, London, 1964.

48

tion. And now, since Christ, we know where lies the future of the noosphere, the future of Man and of all the rest as represented in him: in Christ. Superimposed, then, on what Teilhard called the noosphere, there is the beginning of the Christosphere. 'Christogenesis' is the process through which all men will come to share in, to form part of, the Mystical Body of Christ. And men will bring with them all the rest of that world of nature in which our human nature is inextricably bound up. Christogenesis constitutes the last stage of the evolutionary process. Christ is the term of the natural evolution of all created being. Such a conclusion could only be accepted by one who already had christian faith. But Teilhard's genius will bring many non-believers to the portals of the door of faith.

Teilhard offers a solution, satisfying both to mind and heart (in those rare moments when one really sees) to the perennial christian conflict between the things of this world and those of the next, the conflict between matter and spirit. As Aquinas did for the world of natural learning of Aristotle, so does Teilhard for the modern world of natural science. He grasped the significance of scientific knowledge and steeped himself in it, while at the same time he lived a life of the deepest spirituality, faithful throughout to the spirit and rule of his Order, the Society of Jesus. Faithful too to himself, superbly confident of the essential rightness of his vision. An account has been given[5] of an experience he had at the age of six, which illustrates the clarity with which from the start he saw the unity and goodness of the world of experience. This was the simultaneous appreciation of the significance, the reality, of a piece of iron—a ploughshare—which he was holding, and of the Sacred Heart of Jesus, about which his mother was telling him. The iron was so real, so 'full' of being, so essentially good. So

5. Guitton, Jean, 'Le Phénomène Teilhard', in *Informations catholiques internationales*, 1st Jan. 1960, III, pp. 28-9.

too was the Sacred Heart, fashioned like the ploughshare out of matter. Never in his life, it seems, was he subsequently troubled by or suspicious about matter after the way of Pascal and of the majority of spiritual writers in recent centuries. Cartesian dualism, after the decline of the authentic teachings of St Thomas, bit deeply into christian thinking. Flight from the reality that is the world of nature in search of the things solely of the spirit is surely at the root of the modern predicament. Teilhard shows the falsity of this supposed antithesis precisely by showing how interdependent, inextricably commingled are these two aspects, these two faces, of the created universe. The 'without' and the 'within' are for him two aspects, equally real, of everything that is. It is, I think, 'matter' and 'form' again in modern dress, but with this difference, that everything is seen in terms of duration and hence of evolutionary change.

The sphere of operation of the Divine Spirit is not restricted to Man and the angels. The whole world is involved. As another Jesuit has told us, 'The world is charged with the grandeur of God.' To each of us, thinking in terms of our natural units of measurement, the human frame and the life-span of Man, the world is immensely large and has a history, as has been discovered in very recent decades, which is immensely long. Throughout these aeons, in Teilhard's teaching as in traditional Jewish and Christian teaching, the Holy Spirit has been brooding over the land and over the waters. In this respect the roundness of the world is an essential feature of Teilhard's thought. Being spherical it is essentially a unit, one which progressively turns in on itself and finally discovers the Holy Spirit at the heart of things, Alpha and Omega. This is the source of that inner dynamism which has led through evolution to the development of all the separate 'things' we see around us, to the increasing complexification of the relatively homogeneous stuff of primaeval matter. The manifold and the one. Teilhard was equally conscious of the reality of both.

Attempts to achieve the reconciliation of opposites are everywhere encountered in *The Phenomenon of Man*, and it is astonishing how often the proposed solution rings true even when its formulation is, as perhaps it is bound to be, somewhat obscure and inexact. Take for instance the central problem of randomness versus purposiveness in evolution. The subject really requires a paper to itself. But briefly, evolutionary-theorists can be divided into two groups, of which the first, and much the largest at the present time, stress above all the undoubted randomness of those genetic mutations and recombinations which form the raw material of evolution. The environment too, which acts as the sieve of natural selection, is subject to changes which again appear to be due basically to chance. Complex but meaningless fabrication. Against this sort of approach, some point with justice to the many examples in biological evolution of straight-line development of a species or a group, what is known as orthogenesis. It is then sometimes assumed that this constitutes the basic evolutionary pattern, the guiding force being a kind of 'entelechy', somehow known to the species and inevitably followed as towards a goal consciously perceived. Teilhard, however, speaks of 'groping' as the essential picture of the evolutionary process. The word itself is a stroke of genius. Groping movements are bound to appear to be random, may indeed be so when taken in isolation and without regard to the eventual outcome. Perhaps one might gain some appreciation of his concept by thinking in terms of a highly complex maze, made up of a series of inter-connecting mazes each highly complex in itself and offering to the groping contestants unlimited opportunities for becoming sidetracked into blind alleys. Correct solution of one maze allows the group to proceed to the next. But mere survival at the next stage may require that earlier mazes be reasonably well explored and occupied. Thus the unity of the system as a whole is preserved. With the advent of man the final maze was entered, and the story of man during the last few hundred thousand years is the story of his wanderings and searchings—often seemingly blind—to find the way out. The path was finally lighted for him as recently as two thousand years ago. Teilhard saw this final goal as point Omega. He saw all mankind converging towards it, and together with Man all the rest of creation out of which he has sprung, on which he is entirely dependent for his existence, and for which now he assumes responsibility. Full of understanding of himself and of nature, full of acceptance of all that is, full of love of God and of his creatures.

Is this mere wishful thinking? Is Teilhard so optimistic, so naive, that he can theorise as though no such thing as evil existed? Many, including the present writer,[6] have been misled by his appendix on this subject, where he says, 'Nowhere, if I am not mistaken, have pain or wrong been spoken of.' And yet, on pages 288-290 of *The Phenomenon of Man* he gives a perceptive account of the possibility, always open to Man, of refusal of Omega rather than acceptance. Teilhard is no sentimentalist. There is in him nothing of the 'all things bright and beautiful' approach. Struggle and suffering, pain and limitation, are, for him, simply inherent in the fact of existence. Inherent in the traditional sense of *privatio boni*. With the advent of the noosphere many such deprivations can be overcome, much suffering relieved. But the greater the freedom, the greater the possibilities for both good and evil. It may be extreme, the final anguish of the choice for or against Omega, for or against the evolutionary process itself. A final struggle, between two opposing and irreconcilable groups of men is clearly recognised by Teilhard as a distinct possibility, though one to be prevented by every means in our power. But, what-

6. See below, p. 127.

ever crisis may develop, he is surely right to rest in the christian hope and expectation that finally all shall be well. Incarnation, redemption, resurrection, they cannot have been in vain.

Man has been given—has acquired—tremendous responsibilities as a corollary of the increasing freedom resulting from complexification. Complexification represents increase in the inner-directed 'radial' energy of matter at the expense of the more primitive and outwardly-directed 'tangential' energy such as we see so vividly in the destructive forces locked up in the atom. In the matter of responsibility Teilhard has taken a common picture of the nature of evolution and stood it on its head. We can no longer think of ourselves, as did some of Huxley's audiences in the nineteenth century, as no more than advanced apes with no more responsibility than befits an ape. That is evolutionary regress, not progress. Teilhard, however, is absolutely consistent in his interpretation of the nature of evolution. Further progress can only be through the personal sanctification of the species, personal because, as always, the evolutionary process must actually work through individual members of the species. The conclusion is posited quite soberly by Teilhard, after careful investigation of the facts, of the phenomena. It is expressed in terms of modern science as well as of traditional theology. *The Phenomenon of Man* is certainly the outstanding book of the year, probably of the century, perhaps even of the millennium. With Teilhard christian humanism has taken a great step forward.

Blackfriars, 1960, vol. 41, pp. 119-26.

3

JUNG AND TEILHARD

The writings of Teilhard and Jung have many features in common, those of the one devoted to the macrocosm and the place of Man in it; of the other to the microcosm that is the individual man himself. When the story comes to be written of the development of science in the twentieth century it may well be found that here were two men who played decisive roles in rescuing the scientist, and hence mankind, from the self-contained contradictions to which the logic of the science of the nineteenth century must inevitably have led. The technique of science as it is commonly understood, the method of reductive analysis, that is the explanation of things and events solely in terms of their component parts and antecedents, will always be essential to any understanding of nature. But nineteenth-century scientists, particularly biologists, understandably in reaction against the deist-inspired natural theology of the previous century, fell into the error of supposing, as Epicurus did in his intellectual battles with Aristotle, that explanation in terms of material and efficient causes is not merely necessary (as Aristotle and all of us would agree), but is wholly adequate. The formal cause and the final cause have long been dismissed in the polite circles of 'traditionalists' (as they are fast becoming) as purely metaphysical and hence, in the traditionalist view, quite meaningless abstractions.

One cannot but admire the vigour and enthusiasm with which the apostles of the materialist enlightenment pursued and pursue explanation according to what might be called the 'nothing-but hypothesis'; every thing is to be 'explained' as nothing but a composite of simpler things, themselves reducing to nothing but yet more formless things, until all is reduced to atoms and the void, ultimately chaos. Both Teilhard and Jung have known such apostles intimately in their own spheres of scientific enquiry, and have each borne eloquent testimony, sometimes verbal, sometimes silent, to the admiration and respect in which they have held their colleagues. Without such men the world would be much the poorer in human experience and in knowledge of nature. Accurate, objective analysis of a thing or an event is an essential first step towards understanding it, but cannot of itself provide that understanding. The pathos that we sometimes discern today in the confident, enthusiastic writings of scientists of the past derives not only from our practical experience of some of the horrors of a scientific age wherein there ought, according to the prophets, to be only benefits and blessings, but also from a realisation that all this was somehow necessary, a stage in growing up. Adventurous spirits a hundred years ago were proclaiming in the name of Science the coming dawn of intellectual liberation and, pathetically enough, were welding ever stronger the chains of our present enslavement to a characteristically 'scientific' outlook which is bound to lead the man who holds fast to it to disillusion and despair. Few men have the courage consciously to hold fast; most have too much common sense or too much *joie de vivre* ever to make the attempt, or even to feel the *Angst* of the situation. But whatever one perceives, however vaguely, and thinks to be true, no matter how quickly and with what apparent effectiveness it is banished from the conscious mind, is never wholly lost to the personality. Indeed it may grow there, in the darkness of the unconscious, to prodigious size, and finally demand attention in a way that leaves the sufferer no option. It is well known that the class of scientific research-workers provides a large number of patients for the various schools of depth-analysis.

Both Jung and Teilhard have always claimed to be working in the scientific field of phenomena, to be empirical scientists devoted to purely objective observation, in so far as any observation is ever purely objective—except it be trivial; devoted to the construction of hypotheses on the basis of the observations, and to the testing of the hypothesis by further examination of phenomena in themselves. Each has insisted, however, that true impartiality demands that all phenomena be observed and noted, not simply those that are more readily accounted for in terms of current scientific dogma. Such an attitude is inevitable for a student of the whole, whether the whole is the cosmos itself or the psyche of individual human beings. But the conclusions have been so different from those arrived at in the more usual type of enquiry made by biological scientists, that both Teilhard and Jung have been bitterly accused, by some of their critics, of treason to the cause of science; sometimes contemptuously dismissed as unreliable, outside the scientific pale.

Perhaps the trouble is mainly due to the reintroduction by both of them of the concept of purpose into their accounts of the phenomena they have studied. How distasteful this must be to many heirs of nineteenth-century rationalism can be imagined from a statement made in 1876 by the great Du Bois-Reymond: 'The possibility, ever so distant, of banishing from nature its seeming purpose, and putting a blind necessity everywhere in the place of final causes, appears, therefore, as one of the greatest advances in the world of thought, from which a new era will be dated in the treatment of these problems. To have somewhat eased the torture of the intellect which ponders over the world-problem will, as long as philosophical naturalists exist, be Charles Darwin's greatest title to glory.'[1] But the purpose discerned by our two modern authors

1. Du Bois-Reymond, E., *Darwin versus Galiani*, Berlin, 1876.

is of a different kind from that against which the above protest was made.[2] The purposes seen in natural events by deists of the eighteenth century such as Paley were extrinsic in character, imposed on nature from without by a wholly transcendent deity. The purpose that Jung sees operating within the human psyche is, like that perceived by Teilhard to be operating at the core of the cosmos, intrinsic in character and essentially immanent, immanent in the sense and to the extent that it can be legitimately studied by the methods of natural science.

The story of evolution is the story of the working out of this purpose. Jung is concerned more particularly with the ontogenetic evolution of the psyche, though his theory of the collective unconscious necessarily involves some consideration of phylogeny. For Teilhard a similar sense of immanent purpose imposes itself as a result of study of the evolution of the cosmos: his theme is that of the phylogenetic development of Man. It is in and through Man that this purpose becomes finally manifest. Once perceived in Man, this same purpose is seen as necessarily operating throughout all the countless years of evolutionary time that have led to Man. The whole cosmos becomes involved, just as, in ontogenetic development of the psyche, all parts of the individual's environment are necessarily involved in the formation of the personality. Man is inconceivable without the co-operation of the whole of nature: deprive him of any one of a dozen simple chemical elements, and inevitably his biological existence comes to an end. Deprive him of plant-forms and again, together with the rest of the animal kingdom, he would cease to be. Deprive him of any major part of his normal environment, and his intellectual, moral and aesthetic life would not be, would never have been, possible: where would be the apparatus of the special senses if there were or had been nothing for the special senses to respond to? Deprive him of the past, and he would never have begun

2. For discussion of the meanings of 'telos' see below, chapter 4.

to know the story of his evolution, of his place in nature: it seems that, when one contemplates nature in the round so to speak, one sees that 'they also serve who only stand and wait', even if they have to wait for hundreds of millions of years before being discovered by the palaeontologist.

The goal of life in Jung's eyes is the birth and development, the realisation one might say, of what he has called the Self. For Teilhard the goal is the birth and development, the realisation again, in mankind as a whole, and hence in the cosmos as a whole, of what he has called Omega. The concept of Omega has suffered serious misinterpretation in the hands of hostile critics, both scientific and theological. Not a few have been inclined to dismiss Tielhard as no more than yet another of those emergent evolutionists whose views have provoked moderate interest from time to time ever since the theory of evolution became a happy hunting ground for speculative thinkers. They have tried to account for the appeal which his works are evidently having, for so many people who would not have been taken in by his predecessors, on the basis of a current wide-spread anxiety about future international relations, and of the anxious need for a new optimism to fill the void created by the disillusion of the last two decades. But Teilhard, it seems to me, is in no way visualising a slow emergence of some 'God-in-the-future', the emergence of God out of something not-God or out of something that could be called God only in a pantheistic framework which he expressly repudiates. For Teilhard, God is an ever-living and ever-present reality. He is the source of all being and, in particular, the source of that evolutionary force which, from the beginning of time so far as we can judge, has been gathering momentum against the force of that other stream which we discern in the cosmos, that which leads to increasing entropy. It is significant that Teilhard chose precisely the word Omega in his attempt to convey his meaning. The word carries in one sense, it is true, the meaning of an end-result, a result-in-time, such as has been postulated by emergent evolutionists. But it also implies an end-in-view and, like all such ends, must be in some sense present already. But not only as an idea. Teilhard lays great stress on the fact of Omega as a living reality here and now, a force that has always been. The word Omega is emptied of its most significant meaning if it does not carry with it the sense of Alpha. Alpha and Omega are two aspects of the creator, who is at once immanent in the evolving cosmos and at the same time transcendent to it. The 'emergence', then, of Omega, which Teilhard sees as the major feature of human progress in the future, is an emergence in the proper sense of the term, namely a birth or realisation of something already in existence but hitherto hidden from view (one makes no reference to the question of the possibility, or the fact, of divine revelation), and known in a sense only to mother nature. At Omega-point mankind as a whole will have come to know and accept nature, to know and accept itself, to know and accept God; men united in the charity of understanding, united in the love of all of nature through which they have come to be and without which they would be nothing, united in love of one another, united in love of the God who is Alpha and Omega, the source of all being. The parallel with the birth of the Self in ontogeny is illuminating: the labour in the one case belongs to the individual alone, in the other it is, in St Paul's words, 'the whole of nature' which 'groaneth in travail'.

It is in the notion of a turning-in towards a centre already necessarily existent within, that *enroulement* which Teilhard saw as the essential feature of the evolutionary process, that we perceive strong echoes of Jung, for whom the individuation-process, in the second half of life, is again an *enroulement* in search of the centre of the personality. Though a centre, the Self is at the same time, fittingly enough, the whole. Jung himself has devoted most of his studies to this task of the second half of life, to the final achieving of the goal of individual psychic evolution. This is probably because the problems that arise in this phase of development have been precisely what have induced the majority of Jung's patients to seek his aid. Jung is first and foremost a clinician, and his system of thought is the result of a doctor's attempt both to account for his patients' symptoms and signs and to alleviate their sufferings, their dis-ease. Now it is always dangerous to argue from a study of pathological cases of limited variety to the nature of the normal, especially when the subject of enquiry is one so difficult and complex as the nature of Man himself. But in the present early days of depth-psychology such shortcomings in theory as might result are, perhaps, inevitable, because in the very nature of things the majority of practising therapists will themselves be one-time patients (in the real sense of the word 'patient'), who have achieved whatever maturity and balance they may possess only through a conscientious working-through, in analysis, of their own emotional conflicts and difficulties. The practical experience of analysing the various factors that contributed to a former, frank neurosis, is sometimes regarded as somehow necessary to the making of an analyst. But the argument is clearly false. There is no necessary correlation between the degree of understanding that might be attained and the intensity of personal suffering formerly experienced.

Here we meet with the first of two marked differences between the thought of Teilhard and that of Jung, with which it is intended to close this brief study. For Teilhard the process of *enroulement*, leading eventually to Omega, is one which occurs naturally according to the pattern of the evolutionary process itself—although he recognises that reflective man is capable now of choosing whether to co-operate in the process or to oppose it. He is optimistic enough to suppose that mankind will be neither foolish enough nor wicked enough to defeat the process when it is at last within sight of its goal. For Jung, on the other hand, the birth of the Self necessarily requires, it seems, the assistance of an analyst as accredited *accoucheur*, for, in his view, 'the process of individuation is far from an automatic psychic development.'[3] If this is indeed the case, and if, as seems possible, Teilhard's Omega-point will not be reached until there are many more integrated and fully conscious individuals about than there are today, then clearly professional analysts are going to have an indispensable part to play. But perhaps it will be neither so simple, in one sense, nor so difficult, in another, as that. Jung himself has paid relatively little attention to the process of psychic evolution as it occurs in the first phase of the individual's life, except in so far as it may have been a faulty development, long since past, in the lives of those older patients who have sought his aid. It is in this earlier period that the Ego is differentiated, developed, and finally established. It is perhaps not unlikely that for many of the patients of analytical psychologists the dialogue between the Ego and the Unconscious, which is essential to the realisation of the Self, has proved impracticable or impossible precisely because the Ego was never given a real chance to grow in the way that it must. But for some of those millions who never have cause to concern themselves with this sort of problem it might be quite different. In a recent paper Jacobi[4] has argued, apparently for the first time, that there may be 'a natural process of individuation, occurring without the individual's awareness.' She distinguishes this from that 'deliberately furthered and more or less consciously experienced process of individuation', which is what Jung means by the term.

3. Jung, C. G., *The Integration of the Personality*, Routledge and Kegan Paul, London, 1940, p. 32.
4. Jacobi, J., 'The Process of Individuation', *Journal of Analytical Psychology*, 1958, 3, pp. 95-114.

It may be that there are many ways of discovering the Self. If many of us find it possible to accept and to integrate the unconscious only as adults and under guidance, it may be that the majority of people shift for themselves and, in the normal course of development from infancy to maturity, 'without benefit of any special technique or spiritual direction, achieve the wholeness and wisdom that is granted as the reward of a fully lived-out life' (*loc. cit.*). This is more in keeping with Teilhard's outlook than the views, usually rather gloomy, of many depth-psychologists of all schools, concerning what happens to the psyche if it is left to grow and develop freely, unattended by a vigilant psychotherapist.

One other, and really fundamental, difference between Teilhard and Jung calls for mention in this brief essay. The conflict here, characteristically enough, is the basic one between the individual and the community. Teilhard looks forward ultimately to the development of a sort of world-state, to a practical, existential unity of mankind in which individual desires and strivings will be freely forsaken for the benefit of the community; in which even the consciousness of individuals will somehow be subsumed in a collective 'super-consciousness'. This is one aspect of Omega-point. For Jung, on the other hand, the whole aim of psychic existence is precisely to extricate oneself from the power of the collective: not, it is true, from a collective *super*conscious, but at any rate from that collective *un*conscious in which our psychic life is rooted. The whole of Jungian terminology is orientated towards the uniqueness of the personality, towards the elevation, salvation almost, of the individual. Islands of consciousness, representing the psyches of individuals, are visualised as rising out of the sea of the unconscious. The Jungian aim is to help each little island to become ever more aware, ever more understanding of itself, of the other islands around it, of the sea out of which they have all arisen. In this process the island will grow in area, and will rise higher out of the water. It will achieve greater form and significance, greater distinction. Throughout this development, and more particularly in the later stages, the person concerned will certainly develop more control over his own emotions and reactions, and more understanding of those of others. He will become more tolerant, more benign. But islands can never be other than alone. One who follows this path of 'individuation' may well find himself becoming more and more isolated, more and more lonely in a very deep sense. To give oneself in love to another, and to inspire love in return, requires qualities quite other than calm and tolerant benignity. Seeking and finding the Self is, perhaps, an essential part of the task of achieving personal freedom. But freedom for what? If only to add a little extra bulk to the island of Self, and to help others to do the same, then the process, for all that it seems to lead to sweet reasonableness, is, quite literally, selfish; when the process goes wrong it becomes obviously selfish, as occurs in those unhappy cases of 'inflation' of the personality.

The individuation-process would not, one imagines, have been enough for Teilhard. At some point the Self must abandon itself to the Other. No restriction of individual liberty is here involved. Rather is this the achievement of the greatest liberty known to Man, the freedom to dedicate oneself, whether to a spouse, to religion, to a social or a political movement, to any real vocation. Such dedication, idealism, love, is rightly suspect to analytical therapists, because so often affective states of this kind can be shown, on analysis, to have produced or to be the product of intolerable internal conflicts within the patient's psyche. But the final state of mankind, that of the collective superconscious, will be arrived at not as a result of unconscious identification and 'introjection', but by the free dedication of whole and integrated personalities. It is likely, perhaps, that before mankind arrives at Omega-point the 'natural process of individuation' described by Jacobi will become the norm for many generations of men and women. The Jungian and other schools of depth-psychology, having demonstrated the hazards to which the developing psyche is exposed, and having taught us how to avoid disaster, will have fulfilled their purpose. They will remain in the grateful memory of our descendants.

The Wind and the Rain, An Easter Book for 1962, ed. Neville Braybrooke, Secker and Warburg, London, 1962, pp. 79-87.

4

TELEOLOGY AND THE ANATOMIST

A paper read to the Cambridge University History and Philosophy
of Science Club, 1957[1]

To some, no doubt, the two terms that constitute the title of
this paper will seem to make strange bedfellows. Teleology,
you might think, is a curious speculative anachronism, a
remnant of a long outworn system of Metaphysics, that
discipline that it has been the fashion, at least until recently, in
philosophical circles in this country to decry as meaningless
vapourings on an unknown and in essence unknowable theme.
In complete contrast to this speculative science of abstraction,
Anatomy, you might think, is essentially of the earth, earthy.
It is unhappily true that many otherwise intelligent and well-
informed members of the academic circle still look upon
anatomical science as one that of set purpose limits and confines itself to studies in the mortuary, describing in ever more
bewildering detail the relationships one to another of the
myriad structures that comprise the embalmed human corpse.

1. At the time when my late friend and colleague, the distinguished and de-
lightful philosopher of science, Norwood Russell Hanson (1924–1967) invited me to prepare this paper for the club which he graced as chairman, I was
just beginning to be interested in the writings of Teilhard de Chardin. I did
not, however, feel it wise to refer to his far-reaching theories in this paper,
partly because I did not yet feel sufficiently sure about his interpretations, and
also because his name would at that time have been lost on this particular
audience. My treatment of the concept of teleology is, however, very much in
line with his, and this essay can be taken as background reading to Teilhard's
more developed ideas on the question of 'ends' (in each of the senses here
distinguished) in nature.

Such descriptive study is not, of course, without its own intrinsic interest and value—'know thyself' has from time immemorial been the maxim that points the way to the beginning of wisdom, and no one can deny his body a significant place in the constitution of whatever it is one calls 'oneself'. But if pure description of the details of the inner recesses of the human body were all that constituted anatomy, as some of those not engaged in it still seem to suppose, then such a study, exercising the essentially *sub*-human faculties of visual perception and memory-storing, would lead inevitably to intellectual stagnation; being devoid of theoretical and experimental content it would not indeed even warrant the dignity of the name of Science. This sort of anatomy, it is true, was pursued with great vigour in the Scottish schools of the nineteenth century, and if Continental anatomists paid little heed to this local phenomenon it did have a lamentable if temporary effect in England and the Commonwealth; so much so that a Professor of Anatomy said in a University Address in Adelaide in 1923 that 'of all the members of this little community less is expected of the Professor of Anatomy than of anyone else. He is not expected to be a scholar, he need not be a philosopher, or one erudite, or deeply versed in any branch of abstract learning. So long as he is acquainted with the structure of the human body, as a cabman knows the streets of the city in which he plies for hire, and can impart some of this familiarity to his students, but little more is asked of him.'[2] Now most emphatically this cabman qualification was not *always* the only one required of anatomists, and the last thirty or more years have seen something of a return in this country to the original concept as to what anatomy really is. There was a time, in fact, well on into the nineteenth century, when anatomy was a towering scientific discipline,

2. Wood-Jones, F., Address on 'Anatomy and a Life Principle', printed in a volume entitled *Life and Living*, Kegan Paul, London, 1939, p. 111.

Teleology and the Anatomist

the central pillar of the Faculty of Medicine which itself is by many centuries the oldest of all the scientific faculties in the universities of Western Europe. It would be true to say that the seeds of virtually all the modern biological sciences were contained originally within the one discipline anatomy, and that it is the anatomist who has given birth to each in turn of the main biological disciplines, Zoology (Comparative Anatomy), Pathology (Morbid Anatomy), and Physiology (Functional Anatomy).

The second half of the twentieth century seems likely to see the increasing development of a *synthesis* of the biological sciences, and the question is, which of the present specialties is to constitute the central discipline of the New Biology. Recently a claim has been made by Professor Baldwin the biochemist that his own subject should provide 'a reunification of the biologies' as he puts it.[3] Well, biochemistry is an obvious claimant, and the professor's hopes may well be fulfilled. But I think I am on far firmer ground, and not only because much more firmly rooted in history, in suggesting that, in fact, at the centre of the forthcoming synthesis there will be found the anatomist, paterfamilias of his family of biology, now having gathered together again all his many scientific offspring. The logic of this development of the future is not hard to seek. It was not without reason that anatomy was the first of the biological disciplines, nor that it has been so prolific of others. The first thing that must be done in any scientific enquiry (at least in the science of the macrocosm) is to discover and describe *what* it is one is studying, and so far as animals including man are concerned this means anatomy in the strict sense. But such analysis of the physical make-up of man and other creatures is clearly shot through with questions of a truly scientific nature as to the causes of the features described. The modern anatomist is drawing new strength from his ancient roots,

3. In Newman, J. R., ed., *What is Science?*, Gollancz, London, 1957.

67

established long before the fragmentation and specialisation of
the biological sciences in the nineteenth and early twentieth
centuries, and he is actively preparing for the new era. Research subjects today are legion in Schools of Anatomy. A
recent survey in American schools[4] enquired as to what constituted the major and minor research-interests of the members
of the schools. Of ninety Schools of Anatomy, the following
listed these subjects as being of *major* interest to their groups:
Cytology (studies of the cell) 52%, Electron Microscopy 23%,
Tissue-culture 22%, Histochemistry 53%, Radiobiology 23%,
Embryology 44%, Experimental Embryology 38%, Physical
Anthropology 18%, Morphology 47%, Experimental Morphology 33%, Endocrinology 53%, Neuro-anatomy 74%,
Neurophysiology 40%. Sceptics and unkind critics will say
that anatomists are interested in all these subjects because there
is no longer any intrinsic scientific interest in their own. But
what in fact is happening in anatomy today is biological
synthesis with a vengeance, and an air of confidence is everywhere manifest.

If then I have by now convinced you of the significance of
the second of the two terms in my title, and of the interest of
the modern anatomist in many if not all of biological problems,
what now are we to make of 'teleology'? The word is usually
taken to imply 'design and purpose' in the universe, and for
very many years in scientific circles the term was, and often
still is, a term simply of abuse. To be accused of advancing a
'teleological argument' is often to be judged in orthodox
circles to be guilty of some heinous crime. This was why E. S.
Russell, whenever he gave expression to his rather daring
views about what he calls the 'Directiveness of Organic
Activities', found it necessary to introduce his thesis with an
apologetic phrase such as, 'at the risk of being labelled a tele-

4. *The Teaching of Anatomy and Anthropology in Medical Education*, Association
of American Medical Colleges, Chicago, 1956.

ologist.'[5] So too the late Professor Wood-Jones, who was in some ways one of the more outstanding amongst British anatomists of this century, says with regard to his main thesis in his book *Design and Purpose*, 'From most it is almost certain to receive condemnation as representing an out-of-date harking back to the natural theology of Paley and the days of the outworn doctrines of teleology.'[6] Again, the same author, in *Habit and Heritage*, quotes a review in the *Journal of Anatomy* in which the reviewer says he 'believes such teleological approach to be sterile' (this being on the question, essentially, of the inheritance of acquired characters). Wood-Jones comments, 'The word "teleology" has been for so long a term employed to connote everything that is misguided, old-fashioned and stupid in the interpretation of nature's happenings, that by now, after near a century of this usage, it has somewhat lost its sting, and it is almost refreshing to meet it again in 1942 employed as a stigma of the unpardonable sin.'[7] Now if emotive expressions such as these are to be bandied about by scientists it is clear that tonight we shall be swimming (or drowning) in pretty hot water. Let us look at what teleology actually means.

To most people it means Archdeacon Paley, that eighteenth-century divine whose book entitled *Natural Theology; or, Evidences of the Existence and Attributes of the Deity, collected from the Appearances of Nature* had such a remarkable effect, mostly as I believe for ill, on the development of a proper understanding of these problems. Paley's argument was that all things in nature but especially living creatures were *designed* in the greatest detail by an omnipotent Designer in much the same way that all the complex parts of a watch are designed by the watchmaker. Paley was struck, as every observer of living

5. Russell, E. S., *The Directiveness of Organic Activities*, C.U.P., 1945, p. 3.
6. Wood-Jones, F., *Design and Purpose*, Kegan Paul, London, 1942, p. 75.
7. Wood-Jones, F., *Habit and Heritage*, Kegan Paul, London, 1943, pp. 57-8.

things must be struck, by the phenomenon of 'relation' as he called it, what today in a somewhat different sense we call 'adaptation': every organism seems to be adapted in its physical make-up to the particular environment in which it lives. This suggests at first sight that there is a most intricate and beautiful design manifesting itself everywhere in the quite remarkable mutual 'fitness' observed between organisms of widely differing kinds and their respective environments. Paley saw everything in these terms. Sometimes the argument seems somewhat strained today. So, for instance, he describes the eyes of the mole, eyes which today we see as 'degenerate', and which we think *are* degenerating because this particular organ of perception no longer has survival-value to a creature that has taken to burrowing its way through the ground and which lives in almost perpetual darkness. Paley sees instead evidence of the wisdom of Providence, that has given eyes to the creature but has caused them to be sunk deep in the head and covered over with skin 'in order that' they should not be damaged by the earth in the process of burrowing. He even says that it is the eyes which 'I have always most admired in the mole',[8] and when he asks what it was that brought together eyes like these and feet designed for burrowing in the ground, he answers: 'That which brought together the barrel, the chain, and the fusee, in a watch; design.'[9] Such design as this is what many people still understand by teleology. But let us look at the word a little more closely.

The first part of the word is derived from the Greek *telos*, which means 'end' or, in the adjectival form, 'final'. Now in Aristotle's analysis of nature, there were four conditions considered to be necessary before anything at all could 'be'. Each of these four conditions he called *aitia* and it has been most unfortunate that this word has traditionally been translated as

8. Paley, W., *Natural Theology*, 16th edition, London, 1819, p. 243.
9. Paley, W., *op. cit.*, p. 244.

'cause'. The word 'cause' has a very restricted meaning today, and a much better rendering for modern ears of what Aristotle meant by *aitia* would be 'reason' or 'condition'. There are then four conditions which must be present if anything is to exist, and these are termed the material, formal, efficient and final 'causes' or 'conditions'. W. D. Ross, the Aristotelian scholar, comments that of these four only the 'efficient' and the 'final' 'answer to the natural meaning of cause in English' because, he says, these are 'the two *external* conditions which naturally suggest themselves, the efficient cause or *vis a tergo*, and the final cause or *vis a fronte*.'[10] Now it seems to me probable that to most people the word 'cause' could only be properly applied to the former, the 'efficient', which precedes in time the effect one is considering. The word 'cause' has, for modern ears, undoubted temporal overtones. I suspect that to most people the idea of a *vis a fronte*, of something in the future being a 'cause' of some process now in operation, would seem a contradiction in terms; whereas it does not, perhaps, seem quite so patently absurd if we speak of a final 'reason' or 'condition' for things. In fact, if specific causes produce specific effects, then somehow the effect is inherent and anticipated in the preceding causal network. Aristotle's analysis here provided for mediaeval philosophers the fundamental basis for belief in the existence of order in the universe, that presupposition which all scientists make before setting out on a programme of research: the assumption that all is not chaos, that there are regularities to be observed and laws to be discovered. As to Aristotle's two other 'conditions', the material 'cause' is the very stuff of which things are made, and the formal 'cause', at least in the elaboration of Aristotle's philosophy achieved by the mediaeval schoolmen, is the 'principle of organisation' of the 'stuff', the organisation which determines that it is *what* it is and not something else. Perhaps one of the reasons for the

10. Ross, W. D., *Aristotle*, 4th edition, Methuen, London, 1945, p. 73.

current revival of this philosophy of 'hylomorphism' is that it clearly suits so well the modern physical analysis of all things in the universe in terms of 'energy' (the matter or stuff) and its 'organisation' (or form).

Dr Needham, in his analysis in 1931 of this and other philosophies as they relate to the causal factors involved in the development of embryos says, 'In Harvey's thought the four causes were still supreme; his *De Generatione Animalium* is deeply concerned with the unravelling of the causes which must collaborate in producing the finished embryo. But the end of their domination was at hand . . . Bacon demonstrated that from a scientific point of view the final cause was a useless conception; recourse to it as an explanation of any phenomenon might be of value in metaphysics, but was pernicious in science, since it closed the way at once for further experiments. To say that embryonic development took the course it did because the process was drawn on by a pulling force, by the idea of the perfect adult animal' [I must here interject to observe that this is only one of the many meanings that have been given to the word *telos*—indeed, as here expressed, the notion is not Aristotelian but Platonic, which is a very different outlook indeed] 'might be an explanation of interest to the metaphysician, but as it could lead to no fresh experiments, it was nothing but a nuisance to the man of science. Later on, it became clear also that the final cause was irrelevant in science owing to its inexpressibility in terms of measurable entities. From these blows the final cause never recovered.'[11]

Dr Needham perhaps took too sanguine a view (for his purposes) of the death of teleology in science. Previously, in 1882, Dr Ogle, in a brilliant introduction to his translation of *Aristotle on the Parts of Animals* described the very beginnings of the conflict between the teleologists and the mechanists, as they

11. Needham, J., *Chemical Embryology*, C.U.P., 1931, p. 12.

came eventually to be called. Aristotle of course was the teleologist, arguing against that distinguished predecessor of nineteenth-century materialists, Democritus. Aristotle argued that
the mechanist view, accounting for everything on the basis
only of matter and chance, was inadequate as an explanation
of things. He persistently maintained that as well as material
and efficient 'causes' the formal and the final were also necessary. For Aristotle not one could be dispensed with; and no
single one or combination of two or three of his *aitiai* constituted by themselves an adequate explanation of *anything*.
All four are always essential. But it is certainly true that in
developing his argument against the materialists he was given
to stressing the final cause more than the others. And, further,
his habit of citing biological structures to illustrate his argument led him often away from the central truth of his own
position. Thus he acquired a 'bad' reputation amongst scientists of the last three centuries, a reputation which is largely
unjustified from both the scientific and the philosophical point
of view. Dr Ogle comments on this battle between Aristotle
and Democritus: 'So began, and so was carried on, that venerable strife, which ever since has divided thinking men into two
factions, and which still, though twenty centuries have passed
away, is fought with unchanged weapons, and with increasing
bitterness, and in which neither side has ever succeeded in
reducing an opponent to submission, while each has never
failed to claim complete victory.'[12] Dr Needham, then, was
not the first, in 1931, to think or hope that the theory of final
causes had died the death in biological science. But if it had
indeed died by then, it had taken an unconscionable time about
it, and since 1931 it has undergone a remarkable resurrection.
In recent years, while there has been no lack of publications by
orthodox 'mechanists', there has also been a veritable spate of

12. Ogle, W., ed., *Aristotle on the Parts of Animals*, Kegan Paul, London, 1882,
Intro. iii.

books by eminent biologists in which the concept of teleology has been re-introduced into the very centre of the science. However, as you will see, there are a number of different ways in which different authors have used the concept of teleology. This seems to me to be one of the major sources of confusion about it, a confusion which I hope we can go some way towards clearing up.

We have already mentioned books by E. S. Russell and Wood-Jones. As long ago as 1913 there appeared that most remarkable work, *The Fitness of the Environment* by L. J. Henderson. The author concludes his argument as follows: 'In short, our new teleology cannot have originated in or through mechanism, but it is a necessary and pre-established associate of mechanism. Matter and energy have an original property, assuredly not by chance, which organises the universe in space and time.'[13] In 1942 Sir D'Arcy Thompson, in the second edition of his book *Growth and Form* says: 'Time out of mind it has been by way of the "final cause", by the teleological concept of end, of purpose or of "design", in one of its many forms (for its moods are many) that men have been chiefly wont to explain the phenomena of the living world; and it will be so while men have eyes to see and ears to hear withal';[14] and, lest we think this an expression simply of the frailty of the human mind, he later says: 'Still all the while, like warp and woof, mechanism and teleology are interwoven together, and we must not cleave to the one or despise the other for their union is rooted in the very nature of totality.'[15]

H. J. Muller, in a significant volume entitled *Science and Criticism: the humanist tradition in contemporary thought* pub-

13. Henderson, L. J., *The Fitness of the Environment*, Macmillan, New York, 1913, p. 307.
14. Thompson, Sir D'Arcy, *Growth and Form*, 2nd edition, C.U.P., 1942, p. 4.
15. Thompson, Sir D'Arcy, *op. cit.*, p. 7.

lished in 1943 says: ' "Purpose" is not imported into nature, and need not be puzzled over as a strange or divine something else that gets inside and makes life go; it is no more an added force than mind is something in addition to brain. It is simply implicit in the fact of organisation, and it is to be studied rather than admired or "explained".'[16] This is pure Thomism, though I am sure the author would be surprised if he knew.

R. S. Lillie, in *General Biology and Philosophy of Organism* says: 'The tendency, which still lingers in scientific circles, to deny that teleology exists as an effective factor in nature, or to subordinate it completely to purely physical factors, is largely a survival of the Laplacean or Victorian belief in the completeness and all-sufficiency of physical methods of explanation.'[17] But Lillie's view, in contrast to Muller's, is essentially dualist, because he thinks of the 'end' in terms of a 'preconceived plan' as he puts it; preconceived not, it is true, in the mind of an omnipotent watchmaker (though Lillie would probably allow for this too), but rather preconceived in the psyche of living organisms themselves. New ideas, or 'blue-prints for action', are supposed to crop up from time to time in the history of the evolution of species as the result of psychic events (ideas) in the organism; these blue-prints then, in Lillie's view, are carried into production as in a factory according to what Lillie conceives of as mechanistic causality. Eventually therefore, when the processes are repeated, they are thought to lose their teleological content. Thus he says: 'But in order that any preconceived plan, having at first only a mental existence, should have this result, two conditions are required. First, the plan itself must have a sufficient definiteness and persistence;

16. Muller, H. J., *Science and Criticism: the humanist tradition in contemporary thought*, Yale University Press, New Haven, 1943, p. 109.
17. Lillie, R. S., *General Biology and Philosophy of Organism*, University of Chicago Press, 1945, p. 125.

and second, its presence must in some way influence the course of the physical action without infringing the general physical conditions always present, such as those defined in the laws of energy. The first requirement is the general one of stable factors in all events. The second requirement presents an especially difficult problem, i.e. of how psychical factors can have a directive influence on physical events; here we have the essential problem of teleology, and I know of no way to make this problem entirely simple or easy.'[18] But he eventually concludes that 'the ultimate *locus* of psychical control, in the psychophysical system which is the living organism, is situated *internally to* or behind the elementary physical events (ultimately quantum transfers) which determine the direction of action in the physical field.' Now obviously this is a very different sort of teleology from that of Muller. Muller in fact protests against this dualist form of thinking in the following terms: 'Their (biologists') thinking was long distracted by such antitheses as heredity versus environment, structure versus function, teleology versus causation—antitheses that do not exist in nature but only in our ways of describing nature, and that as subjects of debate are about as pointless as the question of which came first, the chicken or the egg. And behind all such purely verbal issues was the flat opposition between vitalists and mechanists. The vitalists insisted that some altogether new principle—an entelechy, an *élan vital*—was necessary to explain life; the mechanists insisted that the principles of physics were not only adequate but essential. Both tended to lose sight of the living organism in their logical dispute over explanation. Both could have profited by the common sense of William Hunter in the eighteenth century: "Some physiologists will have it that the stomach is a mill, others that it is a fermenting vat, others again that it is a stew-

18. Lillie, R. S., *op. cit.*, p. 129.

pan; but, in my view of the matter, it is neither a mill, a fermenting vat nor a stewpan but a stomach, gentlemen, a stomach." [19] I might perhaps be forgiven for pointing out that William Hunter was an anatomist of the original school!

To continue this brief survey of some recent exponents of those final causes which, if they *are* dead, certainly won't lie down, here is a question from Professor Agar's *Contribution to the Theory of the Living Organism*. After discussion of the significance of organs of perception and their function he says: 'The anticipatory aspect of perception compels us to recognise the reality of final causation in all perceiving organisms. Anticipation implies the power of directing action in accordance with that anticipation; otherwise it would have no function. The function of the capacity of anticipating future occurrences is to influence present action in relation to that anticipation. Causation in this sense is teleological or final causation. It is directed towards bringing about a situation which is not yet existent.'[20] Once again the argument seems to depend on a prior assumption that living organisms are in some way essentially different from non-living, and such an assumption is unwelcome to those of us who have a natural sympathy with monist rather than with dualist interpretations of the things of nature.

Dr L. E. R. Picken, the Cambridge zoologist, writing in 1955 of the significance of final causes in the development of biological structure, says: 'Claude Bernard expressed the opinion that science is not concerned with first causes (origins); he might well have added that scientists are also scared to death of final causes (ends). But it is clear that the biologist at least cannot be indifferent to final causes—to ends—any more than

19. Muller, H. J., *op. cit.*, p. 106.
20. Agar, W. E., *Contribution to the Theory of the Living Organism*, 2nd edition, Melbourne University Press, 1951, p. 18.

was Aristotle himself, whose entire analysis of types of causation is coloured by his biological studies.'[21]

Just how scared scientists have been, and perhaps still are, of ends, was vividly expressed in 1876 by Emil Du Bois-Reymond. In a pamphlet entitled *Darwin versus Galiani* he says (in translation): 'Here is the knot, here the great difficulty that tortures the intellect which would understand the world. Whoever does not place all activity wholesale under the sway of Epicurean chance, whoever gives only his little finger to teleology, will inevitably arrive at Paley's discarded "Natural Theology", and so much the more necessarily, the more clearly he thinks and the more independent his judgement . . . The physiologist may define his science as a doctrine of the changes which take place in organisms from internal causes . . . No sooner has he, so to speak, turned his back on himself than he discovers himself talking again of functions, performances, actions, and purposes of the organs. The possibility, ever so distant, of banishing from nature its seeming purpose, and putting a blind necessity everywhere in the place of final causes, appears, therefore, as one of the greatest advances in the world of thought, from which a new era will be dated in the treatment of these problems. To have somewhat eased the torture of the intellect which ponders over the world problem will, as long as philosophical naturalists exist, be Charles Darwin's greatest title to glory.'[22] Well clearly the intellectual torture has gone on since Darwin. Darwin, in fact, solved only one part of the problem; he left the rest still in some doubt and confusion. The confusion that lies at the heart of Darwinism is well illustrated, in the passage just quoted, by the use of the two phrases, 'Epicurean chance' and 'blind necessity', as

21. Picken, L. E. R., 'The study of minute biological structures', *The School Science Review*, no. 131, November 1955, p. 35.
22. Du Bois-Reymond, E., *Darwin versus Galiani*, Berlin, 1876, pp. 8-9. Quoted Henderson, *op. cit.*, p. 290.

equivalents: when what is 'necessary' becomes equated with what is 'casual' there is a logical muddle indeed. As in so much that has been written on this sort of topic, expressions like 'blind necessity' and 'blind chance' are simply emotive in content: in so far as they succeed in commanding assent they do so only by clouding the reason. Perhaps this was why Du Bois-Reymond was most concerned—though subconsciously I am sure—over the particularly unhappy fate that would overtake those who think 'more clearly' as he puts it.

As a last example of recent biologists to whom the problem of teleology looms large, just a few months ago (1956) there was published a book by E. W. Sinnott, the distinguished botanist and geneticist, with the somewhat disconcerting title *The Biology of the Spirit*. I have selected a couple of passages to indicate something of his approach. 'In simple terms', he says, 'the problem is this: every living thing is an organised system, each part and function closely correlated with all the others. This is evident in many ways, but most conspicuously in the processes of growth and development. A plant or animal grows in an orderly fashion to a precise bodily form characteristic of the particular species to which it belongs, as towards a precise "goal". Growth is so nicely co-ordinated—faster in some directions slower in others—that in all parts it keeps step until the final end is reached. Differences within the organism arise in orderly progression. Development is determined, we know, by thousands of inherited genetic units in each cell, but their actions are so nicely co-ordinated in timing and degree that only rarely do the normal processes become confused. All this is hard enough to understand, but the difficulty is greatly increased by the result of experiments in blocking or interrupting the usual course of development. Under these conditions the organism and its parts show a surprising ability to restore what has been lost, rearrange its normal processes of growth, and produce at last, often by circuitous courses, a whole and typical individual. The whole seems somehow immanent in all its parts. This regulatory capacity is present to a greater degree in some forms than in others, and varies with conditions. It is more evident in early stages of development than in later ones' [we might note here that R. S. Lillie says precisely the opposite] 'but it vividly demonstrates the action of a co-ordinating control of some sort, which guides development to a definite culmination. A living thing is an organised and self-regulating system, well named an "organism". This is a fundamental fact in biology, and the basis for regarding the life sciences as distinct from the physical ones.'[23] It sounds as if he might be an uncompromising dualist, a teleologist with his feet definitely set on the slippery road that leads to Paleyism. But Professor Sinnott is in fact a great deal less naive than was Archdeacon Paley. He says, for instance: 'Biology has only recently won the right to be considered a true science in the modern sense, based on unvarying lawfulness, as physics is, and free at last from childish ideas that plants and animals have human qualities. Scientists have fought so hard to keep the insidious idea of purpose *out* of biology that they will not readily assent to a concept that puts this fighting word back at the very heart of the life sciences. Slipshod teaching has so often falsely appealed to "purpose" that the very word has become anathema to many. One reads in some texts, for example, that roots are "for the purpose" of absorbing water and nutrients from the soil, or that the "purpose" of a fawn's dappled coat is to make him inconspicuous in the forest. A teacher often slips into terminology like this for ease of explanation rather than discussing the more difficult ideas of natural selection or physiological mechanisms. The student thus gets the wrong conception that living things are *trying to adapt themselves* to their surroundings and succeed

23. Sinnott, E. W., *The Biology of the Spirit*, The Viking Press Inc., New York, 1955 and Gollancz, London, 1956, pp. 15-16.

through some mysterious power to do what is best for themselves.'[24]

Sinnott believes that the 'goal' or 'purpose' that he postulates is definitely capable of investigation by science, and that we have a responsibility to investigate it. He continues: 'The . . . goal . . . may turn out to be as mechanical as the "goal" of a thermostat set for seventy degrees. If one wishes to carry this idea to absurdity he may suggest that a stretched bow has a "purpose" to shoot an arrow, or even that a stone has a "purpose" to roll downhill. It may be that purpose can be explained at last in terms of present physical concepts, as have so many other biological problems.'[25] Now the examples which he chooses of a *telos* inherent in inorganic situations would not by any means have seemed absurd to Aristotle nor, *a fortiori*, to Thomas Aquinas. To these thinkers, as we have seen, final causes are *always* necessary for a complete explanation of *anything whatsoever*, living *and* non-living. Mediaeval scholars, following Aristotle, expressed the idea as *Omne agens agit propter finem*. But most of the writers on this subject in the last three centuries have made the final cause very much something of an *extra*, something to be invoked (by those who allowed it at all) only when mechanical efficient causes seemed somehow inadequate. As Theodor Schwann put it in 1829: 'Teleological explanations have long been banished from the physical sciences, and in biology they are only a last resort when physical explanations have proved incomplete.'[26] Now once this position had been taken with regard to teleology, it is obvious that 'teleologists' were destined from then on to be always on the defensive, always retreating back into deeper recesses of biological obscurity before the advancing tide of mechanistic hypothesis and experimental testing. It is no

---

24 Sinnott, E. W., *op. cit.*, p. 63. **25.** *Ibid.*
26. Quoted by E. S. Russell, *Form and Function*, Murray, London, 1916, p. 180.

wonder that teleology became a word of abuse for everything obscurantist and anti-scientific. Professor Sinnott himself, despite his lack of sympathy with the mechanistic biology of yesterday, seems to look upon teleology as very much of an 'extra' rather than, as D'Arcy Thompson put it, being woven 'warp and woof' with mechanism in nature. Sinnott says, in discussing teleology (which he understands in the most obvious of its 'moods'): 'There is always the possibility that "final" causes actually *may* be operative in nature and that a purpose in the mind may have a direct effect on physical events. For such a philosophy our concept of organic purposiveness would provide a biological foundation. Teleology still has its defenders, and among men of science there are some who are unable to account for all the facts of nature without invoking it to some degree. Perhaps the conflict between this concept and the mechanical determinism of science may never be resolved.'[27] One would only comment here that philosophical realists of the Thomist school would say that it is a question not of accounting for *all* the facts of nature without invoking the teleological concept (in a different sense of teleology) but of accounting for *any* of the facts of nature without invoking it.

From all this it is clear that teleology is today very much in the air so far as biologists are concerned. If the anatomist is to play that central role we have suggested for him in the future integration of the biological sciences, it is essential that he be clear in his mind as to what teleology means, and what are its implications. Now from all the quotations I have given you, from general biologists, anatomists, biochemists and physical chemists, there does not emerge any clear single concept of the meaning of *telos* or 'end'. The question can only be answered by asking how the word is *used*, and every writer seems to have used the word in a way different from the others. It

27. Sinnott, E. W., *op. cit.*, p. 67.

is no wonder there is conflict and no wonder that the conflict appears to many to be incapable of resolution. As in all philosophising, the first essential is to clarify and specify the meaning of the terms you use.

Now with regard to the words 'end' and 'final', ambiguity is inherent from the very beginning. When for instance students work towards entry into one of the professions, they come eventually to sit for what is called a Final Qualifying Examination. The word *final* here has two distinct but intimately interwoven ideas, first that of the 'last-in-time' examination, what one might call the 'end-result' of the years of study; but secondly, and in addition, there is implied the idea of a 'purpose' achieved, in that it was with this 'end-in-view', as one might call it, that the study was originally and continually undertaken. Again, when one writes *Finis* (*telos*, end) at the conclusion of a paper or a book, one does so in two distinct senses, first to satisfy oneself that this *is* in fact the end-in-time or end-result of one's labours, but also to give oneself the natural satisfaction of having achieved one's purpose or end-in-view.

These two notions, *end-result* and *end-in-view* are obviously very distinct from one another. But in virtually all authors right from Aristotle himself the word 'end' is used, as it is still today in common speech, now to imply the one thing, now the other, but most often in a mixture of the two in varying proportions. Misconstruction on the part of the reader is inevitable. The history of civilisation is full of bitter conflicts about issues which prove on analysis to be merely verbal; fictitious or non-existent differences of real opinion.

In the discussion which I hope this paper may provoke, it will be important for us to be clear always as to which of several possible categories of meaning we intend the word teleology to have for our particular argument. These I would suggest might be analysed as follows:

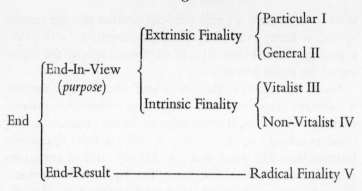

Extrinsic finality implies purpose introduced into the universe from without. *Intrinsic* finality is the purpose which many writers, as we have seen, see as peculiarly evident in and indeed confined to biological systems.

Category I is the 'design' of Paley, in which every single manifestation of nature occurs as the result of a specific purpose in the mind of the deity. Every event has its celestial blueprint as it were. This, in my opinion, is a primitive, magical view of nature, in which the Designer plays the part of magician. The idea is, however, constantly cropping up in otherwise intelligent works, and for a certain type of mind it has obvious attractions.

At the other end of the list, category V implies that every complex of efficient causes produces a result which is inherent in the physical set-up and is therefore reproducible. There is Order and not Chaos. This idea was the greatest single contribution of the Ancients and the Schoolmen to the development of modern science. The world is governed not by Chance but by Law. This notion forms the basis for Aquinas's fifth way of arguing towards the necessary existence of something which, as he puts it, 'we call God'.

Categories III and IV include all those theories of the last hundred years of 'emergent' and 'creative' evolution, the notion of an inner entelechy (the word is Aristotle's) directing biological processes, a force which many biologists regard as necessary to account for biological 'adaptation'. Amongst modern exponents of the 'new' *directiveness of organic activities* we might, I suppose, have to include Russell and Lillie as exponents of category III, and perhaps Muller and Sinnott in category IV. But you will of course realise, from what was said earlier, that it is not easy to pin down the meaning which any particular author intends the word 'end' to have, and Sinnott, as we saw, seems to combine vitalism and non-vitalism in a remarkable way.

Category II interests me most. It implies that there *is* some overall divine end-in-view or purpose in the universe, but that the purpose works in and through the operation of scientific law (except, for a christian perhaps, in so far as miracles are concerned). It seems to me that Henderson, and possibly D'Arcy Thompson, argue in an inductive way towards this conclusion, and I find their accounts intellectually compelling. But this category of meaning of teleology could be arrived at logically, I think, from analysis of the implications of category V, though it would require a cool head.

Now how might anatomists in general be expected to react to each of these categories? (I can, of course, speak only for myself). How far should we be inclined to say that the detailed structure of our bodies (and the human anatomist knows a lot of detail) is evidence of heavenly blue-prints? How far is it the achievement of an *immanent* purpose working in and through the physical, drawing on the developing body towards an end foreseen and somehow desired? How far is it the inevitable end-result of that particular complex of causal chains and causal networks that have contributed, throughout the ages of evolutionary development and throughout the months of embryological development, to the formation of the human being as we know him, through the operation of scientific

laws which surely await elucidation by our scientific descendants if not indeed by us ourselves to some extent? With this
last he will certainly, as would any scientist, find himself in
sympathy. Indeed it is to the elucidation of the laws that
govern the development of anatomical structure (the science
of morphogenesis as it is called) that the main research-work
of the anatomist is directed. Now of course, like any scientist,
he can content himself with simply doing this work if he
wishes, and never even question his underlying assumption
that there *are* causal laws of morphogenesis to be discovered.
As Henderson has said: 'The chemist puts his mind at rest
regarding the existence of life, just as the physicist calms his
regarding the existence of matter, simply by turning his back
on the problem. Thereby he suffers nothing in his practical
task as a man of science.'[28] But if we want not only to *know*
something about nature but also to try to *understand* it, in so
far as this is possible, then we must take the plunge, as we have
done tonight, into philosophy.

As for my category I, there would surely be few anatomists
(the late Professor Wood-Jones perhaps amongst them) who
would find themselves in sympathy with this form of teleology. The degenerate eyes of the mole are not, so far as we
can see, exquisitely planned, as Paley supposed, but are degenerating because they no longer have survival value to the
species (or as a result of some other as yet unknown causal
factor in evolutionary development). If even the human eye,
about which exponents of this sort of teleology are wont to
enthuse, were planned by a divine Designer, then one would
have sympathy with Helmholtz in his views on what a de-
fective instrument it is even at best, and profound sympathy
with all those who happen to have been supplied with what in
industry today would be classed as 'export rejects'. The
anatomist, as we have said earlier, is very much a part of the

28. Henderson, L. J., *op. cit.*, p. 310.

medical profession, and it is our job as doctors to know something not only of physiology but of pathology. The realisation that human beings and other living organisms have a *pathology* as well as a *physiology* is second-nature to the anatomist who fathered, as we said at the beginning, both these sciences. The pathologist, or morbid anatomist, is not nearly so inclined to wax enthusiastic about the 'immanent purpose' in living things (categories III and IV)—he knows too much about the obvious *lack* of immanent purpose in the disease-processes that bring his subjects to the post-mortem room. Now until very recently there has been virtually no science of general as distinct from human pathology. General biologists, who have grown ecstatic over the seeming purposiveness of the creatures they have studied, are in for quite a surprise when they come to realise how expertly nature has hid from their view its failures, and showed them only its successes. Again, take embryology. The general biologist may radiate confidence about the wonderful purpose he sees continually at work in the developing embryo of the frog. But whenever a human embryologist is studying his serial sections through his microscope, he cannot help but be conscious that here on the slide is or was a fellow human-being who, for one reason or another, had insufficient of this supposedly all-pervading purpose or will to live. The proportion of fertilised human ova which fail to survive, from natural causes, is of staggering dimensions. In addition, there are those hundreds of different kinds of congenital abnormalities, leading to death or severe disfigurement, which the anatomist is continually being asked by his colleagues in the Department of Pathology to help elucidate from the embryological point of view. Categories III and IV begin to look a little different in the light of these facts. In his Terry Lectures entitled *Ourselves Unborn: an Embryologist's Essay on Man*, Professor George W. Corner said, at the conclusion of a moving chapter on 'Prenatal Fate and Foreordination': 'Those of us who survive are truly the elect, chosen from a larger multitude. In this fact we may take a melancholy pride, like soldiers who close the ranks and march on when their companions fall. Let us make all we can of this life; we are fewer than we thought.'[29]

To end on a less sombre note, it has been said that all scientists have a secret passion for teleology but that, like a mistress, she has to be kept out of sight of polite company. For myself, I would be happy to take her into public as a respectable married woman and call myself openly a teleologist, provided that I am allowed to specify in what senses I am using the term. As to specific divine purposes as manifested in particular structures and events in nature, I would say, so far as philosophical enquiry is concerned, with René Descartes: 'In the admirable purpose assigned to each part, both in plants and animals, it is proper to admire the hand of God who made them, and by an inspection of the work, to know and praise the Author; but we cannot surmise for what purpose He created each particular thing.'[30]

Blackfriars, 1957, vol. 38, pp. 355-64 and 408-17.

29. Corner, G. W., *Ourselves Unborn: an Embryologist's Essay on Man*, Yale University Press, New Haven, 1944, p. 122.
30. Descartes, *Principles* I, 28.

5

SCIENTIFIC MASTER VERSUS PIONEER:
MEDAWAR AND TEILHARD

BBC Third Programme Talk, 1965

It is just over five years since the publication of Teilhard de Chardin's book *The Phenomenon of Man*. At about the same time, the fifth volume of his collected works appeared in France: this has recently been translated (1964) and published here as *The Future of Man*. The title is familiar; it is the one Dr P. B. Medawar chose for his distinguished Reith lectures—and it was while those lectures were being broadcast, in the closing months of 1959, that *The Phenomenon of Man* attracted widespread notice in this country. Medawar later emerged as our chief critic of Teilhard, and I cannot help feeling, in the light of subsequent events, that one sentence from his concluding Reith lecture[1] has a special significance.

Medawar was here at last embarking on his title-theme, having spent the first five lectures emphasising, with a wealth of illustration, the fallibility of statements about the future. He introduced the discussion with these words: 'The attempt must be based upon hard thinking as opposed to soft thinking; I mean, it must be thinking that covers ground and is based upon particulars, as opposed to that which finds its outlet in the mopings or exaltations of poetistic prose.' That the Reith lecturer had Teilhard in mind became fairly obvious when, some twelve months later, his famous (or notorious) attack was published. The January 1961 issue of the philosophical

1. *The Listener*, 24th December, 1959.

journal *Mind* contained no fewer than eight pages of dazzling invective, under the heading 'Critical Notice of *The Phenomenon of Man*'. Rarely if ever can that staid and erudite little journal have bristled and sparkled with such a display of verbal fireworks.

'Mopings or exaltations of poetistic prose' (a hard-hitting expression in itself) now gets even more punch as 'tipsy, euphoric prose-poetry'. The article was full of clever phrases of this sort. As entertainment it was undoubtedly first-rate. If some of us regretted Medawar's indulgence in what could with justice be described as highly emotional parody, there were others who thought it a particularly fine piece of debunking.

One might regard this sort of criticism, by a scientific particulariser, of a scientific generaliser, as only a variant on that fierce battle between what Ved Mehta called the 'dry-biscuit' historians and their 'plum-cake' colleagues.[2] But we must be careful not to draw too close an analogy. Science tends naturally to be a 'dry-biscuit' subject. Teilhard was as dry and particular as anyone could wish in more than 150 scientific papers published during his career. His plum-cake has some pretty hard, dry bits in it, too. It is significant that biological scientists of the eminence of Thorpe in this country, Piveteau in France, and Dobzhansky in America regard Teilhard as a seminal force of great significance to science. Ved Mehta, having surveyed the battlefields in history and philosophy, concluded that 'unless a philosopher finds for us an acceptable faith or synthesis . . . we remain becalmed on a painted ocean of controversy.' But to be effective for our civilisation such a synthesis must, it seems to me, be firmly rooted in the natural sciences. And I think that Teilhard de Chardin provides the necessary basis.

2. Mehta, Ved, *Encounters with English Intellectuals*, Weidenfeld and Nicolson, London, 1961.

Medawar subsequently enlarged his attack, in his 1963 Herbert Spencer lecture, to embrace all those who have been what he calls 'system-builders' about evolution. Spencer himself came in for some pretty severe comment, but, as was perhaps only right in the circumstances, he got it in a kindly if somewhat patronising way. He is represented as a sort of Victorian fuddy-duddy, chugging along in what Medawar regards as 'steam-philosophy'. With a reference to the *Mind* article, Teilhard is now contemptuously dismissed in these words: 'Teilhard, on the contrary, was in no serious sense a thinker. He had about him that innocence which makes it easy to understand why the forger of the Piltdown skull should have chosen Teilhard to be the discoverer of its canine tooth.'[3] Medawar's mission appears to be complete, his adversary utterly routed. But can it really be as simple as that?

The works of eminent scientists, like those of eminent men in other fields, fall into one of two categories. There are the works of the pioneers and the works of the masters. Both are essential, for they are wholly complementary. I intend no slight to either in saying that Teilhard is unquestionably a pioneer, and that Medawar is one of today's masters of science. And I do not want to suggest that a man may not be partly both. But the advances made by a master—and they are often big and important ones—are always in limited fields, and they fall within the accepted framework of ideas. And of course a pioneer, if his work is to be of any value, must first acquire mastery over his subject. We are not surprised, perhaps, that in the more subjective disciplines like painting and architecture, poetry and play-writing, pioneers should meet with criticism from masters, and this even when the innovators are genuine —for the whole business is open to self-deception and to fraud.

3. Medawar, P. B., 'Onwards from Spencer: Evolution and Evolutionism', *Encounter*, September, 1963.

But people seem to think that in science, at any rate, everything is so objective and logically controlled that even big jumps always come about smoothly, and are accepted in gentlemanly fashion. The myth that science works through a wholly inductive process of reasoning has long since been exploded by Popper, Braithwaite, and Polanyi. Nevertheless, when we think of the heated reactions which have greeted new scientific insights, as for instance with the Copernican and the Darwinian controversies, we tend today to think of the conflict as being, throughout, between scientists on the one hand, representing (to some people at any rate) forces of light and progress, and theologians, philosophers, and literary men on the other, representing forces of darkness and ignorance.

But it does not really work like that. The initial opposition to Copernicus and Galileo came not from theologians but from university professors, master astronomers and mathematicians, the scientific establishment of the period. So too with Darwin. When his book was published in 1859 it was no less a person than Professor Sir Richard Owen, the most knowledgeable anatomist of his day and a distinguished pillar of academic society, who was behind what William Irvine called 'the venomous and confused counter-attacks' against the theory of evolution.[4] Darwin himself says in his autobiography that he felt his ideas would not be tolerated by entrenched scientific orthodoxy. In the event he was wrong in his judgement of the climate of scientific opinion. Evolutionary ideas had been floating round long enough to ensure that some scientists would speak out in his defence. But Darwin was right to fear the masters. When any discipline has at its disposal a large corpus of established knowledge, it is virtually certain that the outlook of most of its leaders will be, in important matters, reactionary. When new concepts show great daring and

4. Irvine, William, *Apes, Angels and Victorians*, Weidenfeld and Nicolson, London, 1955.

originality, then conflict, often with high emotional content, is the rule.

So pioneers in science must always be prepared for harsh criticism from their fellows. As Sherrington, both master and pioneer in neurophysiology, drily remarked when consoling a colleague who had suffered abuse: 'Why, in science we put up an Aunt Sally and say, "Here a penny a shy." '[5] It requires courage to put up for attack the truly creative hypotheses which mark big scientific advances. Teilhard was sufficiently advanced in self-knowledge, and in rigorous self-honesty, to speak of his international reputation as a master of his scientific discipline, as constituting a 'platform' from which he hoped to get a hearing for his creative thinking. The scientific honours he received in his lifetime, and the obituaries that appeared in the professional journals, are sufficient guarantee of the soundness of his platform.

The fundamental pioneering achievement of Teilhard was to make sense out of the two most famous, but apparently contradictory, scientific ideas to come out of the nineteenth century: the theory of biological evolution on the one hand, and the second law of thermodynamics on the other. The real implication of a world picture derived from these two concepts was never, perhaps, better expressed than by Sherrington in 1937:

The living energy-system, in commerce with its surround, tends to increase itself. If we think of it as an eddy in the stream of energy it is an eddy which tends to grow; as part of this growth we have to reckon with its starting other eddies from its own resembling its own. This propensity it is which furnishes opportunity under the factors of evolution for a continual production of modified patterns of

5. Quoted in *Physiologist, Philosopher and Poet* by Lord Cohen of Birkenhead, Liverpool University Press, 1958.

eddy. It is as though they progressed toward something. But philosophy reflects that the motion for the eddy is in all cases drawn from the stream, and the stream is destined, so the second law of thermodynamics says, irrevocably to cease. The head driving it will, in accordance with an ascertained law of dynamics, run down. A state of static equilibrium will then replace the stream. The eddies in it which we call living must then cease. And yet they will have been evolved. Their purpose then was temporary? It would seem so.[6]

In his lecture on 'The Two Cultures', Lord Snow[7] charged the literary camp with ignorance of science in general, and of the Second Law in particular. It may be true that few arts dons could quote the law with strict accuracy and economy of expression, but it is a fallacy to think that it has not been fully understood by the literary world, or that it has not had a profound impact on the literary culture of the last half-century. The eighteenth and nineteenth centuries quietly gave up the idea of personal immortality because they were fascinated by the idea of progress. The reward for endeavour was the betterment of mankind and all the high humanitarian ideals that that gave rise to. For a time the theory of evolution appeared to give scientific support. Unhappily, in the latter part of the last century biological theory fell into a decline, precisely at the time when the physical sciences were in the ascendancy. The Second Law, or Law of Increasing Entropy, began to dominate the minds of those who had the courage to take it seriously. The idea that because of the very nature of things the only possible ultimate future for man is annihilation, has crept like a paralysis through our culture. Some of the less discerning,

6. Sherrington, C., *Man on his Nature*, the Gifford Lectures 1937-38, C.U.P., 1941.
7. Snow, C. P., *The Two Cultures*, the Rede Lecture, C.U.P., 1959.

especially among scientists, may still prattle on about scientific progress and the like. The literary culture has understood more clearly, and grasped more honestly, the real implications of Sherrington's scientific world picture.

Important writers in modern literary and philosophical movements have accepted this profoundly pessimistic vision as the true one. Mankind as a whole is a dead duck. Significance must be sought, if at all, in analysis of the isolated individual— and this at a time when the individual, once he has arrived at his own most certain death, is looked upon as no more than a bag of bones undergoing the much more probable process of thermodynamic decay. Much existentialist philosophy, and many of the anti-social and anti-humanist attitudes in modern literature, can be accounted for, in part at least, by considerations such as these. We have been led astray by the inadequate scientific understandings of the past.

Schrödinger, the great physicist, spoke of the nineteenth-century scientific attitude in his posthumous book *My View of the World*:

Call to mind that sense of misgiving, that cold clutch of dreary emptiness which comes over everybody, I expect, when they first encounter the description given by Kirchhoff and Mach of the task of physics (or of science generally): 'a description of the facts, with the maximum of completeness and the maximum economy of thought'; a feeling of emptiness which one cannot master, despite the emphatic and even enthusiastic agreement with which one's theoretical reason can hardly fail to accept this prescription. In actual fact (let us examine ourselves honestly and faithfully), to have only this goal before one's eyes would not suffice to keep the work of research going forward in any field whatsoever.[8]

8. Schrödinger, E., *My View of the World*, C.U.P., 1964.

Concerning Teilhard

I am reminded of Teilhard's words:

> If progress is a myth—that is to say if, faced by the work involved, we can say: 'What's the good of it all?'—our efforts will flag. With that the whole of evolution will come to a halt—because we are evolution.[9]

Sherrington resolved the dilemma to his own satisfaction by adopting a Cartesian dualism of mind and matter, a philosophy which I venture to think will never again capture the imaginations of the majority of men. Schrödinger solved it with what is to me a retreat into an eastern vision of mind as the unifying, and indeed unitary, principle of all that is real.

Medawar himself looked at the problem—somewhat sketchily, as he admits—towards the end of his Herbert Spencer lecture. One thing he concluded was that we really need different kinds of language to deal with the concepts proper to biology and those proper to thermodynamics. One thinks at once of Teilhard's brilliant pioneering neologisms, such as 'radial' and 'tangential' energy, phrases devised precisely to meet some at least of the difficulties.

Of all the original hypotheses invented by Teilhard, the central one is that which he stated as the 'law of increasing complexity-consciousness'. According to Teilhard, to see in matter only a fundamental tendency towards increasing randomness, and to explain away all evolutionary phenomena as the chance play of currents and eddies in the stream of entropy, is to blind oneself to another trend in nature for which research in the last few decades has produced overwhelming evidence. Over a period of at any rate many hundreds of millions of years—and that is a period of time which on any reckoning cannot be explained away as a minor current or

9. Teilhard de Chardin, Pierre, *The Phenomenon of Man*, Collins, London, 1959.

eddy—there has been a steady increase in the complexity of the stuff of this world. Together with this 'complexification' of matter there has been a steady rise, not only in the number of conscious elements in the world, but also in the levels of consciousness they have attained. The system holds together, because higher levels always depend on lower levels of organisation being adequately represented.

Teilhard defines consciousness as 'the specific effect of organised complexity'. One can quote individual examples (though they are relatively rare, except on time scales too small to be significant) where the trend appears to have been halted or even reversed. This is not orthogenesis in the old, suspect sense. But it is less perverse, and a good deal more rewarding, to regard *these* reversals as currents and eddies in a stream leading towards increased consciousness than to argue, as before, that human self-consciousness, for instance (the highest level so far achieved), is no more than a chance epiphenomenon thrown up in a particularly confusing eddy in the stream of increasing entropy. Teilhard takes a historical view of the world, as only an expert geologist and palaeontologist can. He backs his law with a wealth of scientific evidence—despite its Gallic mode of expression. It is founded on local observations; that is to say, on observation of the world in which we live. But there is a degree of generality about it that makes it applicable to matter anywhere in the universe: and this, I submit, is characteristic of a really great pioneering concept. Certainly no one could predict how what he calls the internal propensity of matter to unite, to become more complex and therefore more conscious, would manifest itself in particular circumstances. But the theory obviously allows, for instance, for the probability—indeed virtual certainty—of intelligent beings on other planets. It has relevance to proven phenomena in the field of extrasensory perception. It could give a reason why experts in the modern science of cybernetics could in principle devise electronic computing machines sufficiently complex to be able to solve problems of their own devising, problems beyond the power of individual men to devise. These phenomena would be for Teilhard still further elaborations, wholly to be expected and desired, of what he called the noosphere or 'thinking layer' of the world.

In a talk in the Third Programme[10] some months ago it was suggested that the importance of Teilhard lay in the fact that he had given back to man the virtue of hope. The speaker recalled the myth of Pandora's box, and found a source of strength, which one applauds, in reflecting that this was the only virtue that Pandora managed to save for man. But I think that he did Teilhard rather less than justice. The law of increasing complexity-consciousness is far more than an unreasoned hope for the future. The law is scientific in the real sense, that is, open to verification. If it is tested and found to be valid, and if its implications are accepted, then the ultimate physical death postulated by the second law of thermodynamics will be seen to have lost its sting.

When new pathways have been cut by a pioneer into the jungle of ignorance that surrounds our little human clearing, the masters in the community can do one of two things: they can either sit tight in their well-cultivated civic gardens, and try to persuade other members of the community to ignore the benighted traveller, with his tall tales of what lies beyond the pale; or they can listen to him, even go with him some distance, help to clear the weeds, straighten the paths, and enlarge the area under cultivation. This is the only way, in fact, that science and civilisation have ever advanced. There are signs that this century will do for Teilhard de Chardin what we are still doing for Darwin. Teilhard himself, at the end of *The Phenomenon of Man*, says: 'I may have gone astray at many points. It is up to others to try to do better.' Dobzhansky

10. Wormald, B. H. G., 'Progress and Hope', *The Listener*, April 9, 1964.

ended his recent book, *Mankind Evolving*,[11] with a quotation from Teilhard which reads, in Dobzhansky's own translation, as follows:

> Man is not the centre of the universe as was naively believed in the past, but something much more beautiful—Man the ascending arrow of the great biological synthesis. Man is the last-born, the keenest, the most complex, the most subtle of the successive layers of life. This is nothing less than a fundamental vision. And I shall leave it at that.

The Listener, 1965, vol. 73, pp. 557-63.

11. Dobzhansky, T., *Mankind Evolving*, Yale University Press, New Haven, 1962.

6

LIFE BEFORE BIRTH: HUMAN EMBRYOLOGY AND THE LAW OF COMPLEXITY-CONSCIOUSNESS

A paper read to the First (1966) Annual Conference of the Teilhard de Chardin Association.

It is reasonable to suppose that the problem of his origin is one that has intrigued man ever since he became capable of self-reflection. The question of group-origin (phylogeny) seems to have interested primitive man more than that of individual origin (ontogeny), a point which is significant for the analogies we shall be making between the two types of 'development'. But the latter, which constitutes the subject of embryology, must also have caused man to wonder from his early days. It is not without significance that small children go through a period of intense curiosity (which is not at all prurient) on the subject of where babies come from. The myths and lies that their enquiries have so often elicited in recent centuries represent one aspect of the failure of Western civilisation, and christianity in particular, to respect an honest search for truth and its normal means of communication through natural phenomena. If one does not respect honest enquiry, then distortion of truth is inevitable. Anyone who looks through distorted spectacles for any length of time is likely to have his vision permanently affected. Amongst adults today, including many, of course, who are themselves fathers and mothers, there is astonishing ignorance of some of the basic facts concerning human embryological development. Errors of interpretation abound. One does not expect everyone to become an embryologist, but he ought at least be informed about some of the fundamental conclusions of this branch of medical science.

The subject is not the easiest to study or to comprehend. Like all the biological sciences, but to a greater degree than many of them, it is complicated by the fact that the time-dimension is of crucial importance. Most things in nature are difficult enough to analyse even when they stand still (in so far as anything in nature ever does stand still). But when there are whole series of inbuilt and progressive changes occurring in living-organisms along a time-axis whose intervals are comparatively brief, then they become very difficult to handle conceptually. Our thought-processes tend to have a great inertia about them. This is perhaps because we experience ourselves as somewhat static creatures, and after all it is we who engage in thought-processes. We feel, know ourselves to be, today, very much the same as we were yesterday, and as we expect to be tomorrow. The pace of life, and our appreciation of the speed of change, may vary according to the particular period through which we happen to be living at the moment, and to the degree of interest (or lack of it) and happiness (or lack of it) that we are currently enjoying. But most people recognise no great change in themselves from day to day, or even from year to year. We must all have had that curious experience of meeting a group of acquaintances from the past, and being struck by how much more *they* all have changed than we have ourselves.

Now an embryo is unable, or so it would seem, to reflect upon itself in these terms, and on the developmental changes it undergoes. But if it could, it would see more change in itself in a day than we see in ourselves in a decade. Later I shall outline the type and speed of changes that occur. For the moment let us merely reflect that if all life can be legitimately thought of as a journey towards death there can be no doubt that the speed of travel measured in biological time, that is by the speed of biological change, is fastest in the embryo. Subsequently there is a gradual deceleration unless and until one of a small group of illnesses overtakes one. The embryo, as a professional colleague of mine once observed, rushes headlong not merely towards independent life but also towards the grave. It is perhaps as well we don't keep up that pace.

This was all by way of introduction to the difficulties inherent in what is pre-eminently a four-dimensional study. The key to modern understanding of natural phenomena lies in the proper appreciation of the dimension of time. We know now, from our recognition of the evolutionary process, that time is not merely one more component of the static or the cyclical. But Western European culture developed for over two millennia with the notion that time, like length and breadth and depth, could be divided up indefinitely into smaller and smaller portions. The concept of the 'atom' or 'that which cannot be divided', was as much a puzzle for our forebears as are subatomic particles to the average man today. Scholars used to toy with the notion that if one only thought about it logically enough one would see that an arrow shot from its bow ought never to reach its target because of the indefinitely divisible nature of both space and time. The notion is clearly fallacious, but it is difficult to fault it logically on traditional Western premises about the nature of things. As a professional anatomist I might perhaps be allowed to say that, much as I value the detailed knowledge that has resulted from our anatomising and analysing (literally cutting up and loosening up) everything we come across, yet one result of the habit is much to be regretted: as small boys quickly learn, it is much easier to take things to pieces than to put them back together again. Performing an anatomy or analysis is only the first step towards understanding. Nothing is fully understandable except it is seen in its wholeness, and any individual part makes ultimate sense only in the relation it bears to the whole.

It is a somewhat unnerving experience to browse around in the field of the history of embryology (as you may do, for instance, in Dr Joseph Needham's classic book of that title).[1] For all man's natural interest in the processes of generation, and discounting the occasional insights of men of genius, the truth is that until as recently as a hundred years ago (that is, well into the Scientific Age) the most absurd errors in observation, and crass misinterpretations, were still being made concerning embryos. Of course it is only comparatively recently that biology emerged from the status of a branch of natural history to become one of the natural sciences. This was when it acquired, and finally accepted after many battles, the unifying and stimulating Darwinian hypothesis of evolution. One can still read with profit pre-evolutionary works in some branches of biology. In the works of Richard Owen, say, or in the lectures of John Hunter, one marvels at the range of knowledge displayed, and at the acuteness and accuracy of the observations they made. But what is one to say of their contemporaries amongst embryologists who, long after the discovery of the microscope (the lack of which might be held to excuse earlier workers), were divided into two such incompatible groups as the so-called Ovists and Animalculists? The first group held that the embryo was entirely the product of the maternal egg, for which the male provided only a stimulus. The second group saw, or thought they saw down the microscope, a complete miniature human being in every spermatozoon, awaiting only the fertile soil of the womb to become animated and start to grow. This idea of the nature and power of the male seed is, of course, a very ancient one. It probably provided the basis for one rationalisation of ancient conquering tribes. They would slaughter the male members

1. Needham, J., *History of Embryology*, 1934, 2nd edition, C.U.P., 1959.

of the defeated group, in order to prevent admixture of foreign blood, but would take the females into captivity and breed with them. Although the mother of a child clearly had an influence on her baby before as well as after birth, it was believed that the practice did not put into jeopardy the purity of the race, because it was only the male seed that was thought to give rise to the offspring itself. The Animalculists were their natural successors in a scientific milieu. By contrast, the Ovists were out-and-out feminists. One doubts if anyone holds such views as either of them today, but others equally erroneous are clearly present in the popular imagination.

I speak of these things not for the sake of recounting items of folklore and myth, but to emphasise the point that modern understanding of embryological development is of very recent origin, and as yet we have only scratched the surface of the subject. Doubtless we are today still making faulty observations, and drawing faulty conclusions. One only hopes that our descendants will recognise them as honest errors, such as were made in this field by the great William Harvey. He might well have made embryological discoveries that subsequently lay hidden for two hundred years more, if he had not chanced, because of the opportunities afforded him during the Royal Hunts, to investigate early mammalian development in deer, one species of which has the curious trick of holding the fertilised ovum in a state of suspended animation for weeks after breeding, before embryological development begins. Harvey was quite misled as a result. Other honest errors of interpretation, made by earlier scientists, include that of the fact that sometimes a hen's egg, immediately after laying, can be seen down the microscope to have a minute but distinct embryological form within it. This fact, together with the observation that hens lay fertile eggs for up to three weeks after mating, provided strong arguments for the Ovists, who held that the function of the male was simply to provide a 'fecundating influence' on the female, who then produced fertile eggs for as long as the influence persisted. The occasional, and valid, observation of some kind of embryological form immediately after the egg was laid made them at one with the Animalculists in accepting 'preformation' as against the alternative hypothesis of 'epigenesis' in embryological development. Their errors stem from the fact that they were not to know how long avian spermatozoa from a single ejaculation can survive to fertilise a succession of eggs. Nor did they know how many hours sometimes a fertilised egg will remain in the oviduct before laying, thus allowing for development of recognisable embryological form prior to its accessibility for investigation. These are, therefore, what I call honest errors, such as are recognised as part and parcel of scientific life. They are always corrigible. Their correction depends not only on improved observation, but also on a readiness, which is basic to all true scientists, though not, of course, invariably practised, to recognise mistakes and to lose no time in rectifying them.

It is not so easy to forgive the other major source of the many errors in the history of human embryology. Few sciences have been so bedevilled by ignorant, unwarranted speculation. By this I mean the application of metaphysical or theological principles or beliefs to natural phenomena prior to their objective examination simply as phenomena. Or, alternatively, the acceptance of one scientific hypothesis and the rejection of another because of philosophical or theological predilections, and the subsequent incorporation of the preferred *schema* into some kind of theological orthodoxy. The Church's position on the nature of sex and the ethics of contraception would have been very different if corrigible scientific hypotheses had not been so affected, one way or another, by authoritarian theological considerations. Theological premises must never be allowed to predetermine what is to be admissible as evidence concerning natural phenomena. Theology is still queen of the sciences, but she must learn to behave as a constitutional monarch and not an autocrat. If theologians wish to speculate about the status of the embryo they should first learn some embryology at first hand in the laboratory. (So too, of course, should politicians who wish to legislate for the destruction of embryos by artificial abortion.) In the seventeenth and eighteenth centuries theological fashion insisted that those who taught the Aristotelian theory of epigenesis, that is that an embryo undergoes gradual development involving changes of shape and increasing complexity of organisation, were little better than atheists. The preformation theory was preferred, and is perhaps the reason for the popularity in sophisticated circles of the 'homunculus', as the mythical little man in the spermatozoon was called. Not all of these errors are of the honest kind. This is an ever-present danger, against which we must always be on our guard.

Real advances in embryological knowledge came in the second half of the nineteenth century. In view of the enormous interest during the same period in evolutionary theory, it is not surprising that parallels were drawn between ontogenetic and phylogenetic development. There are, indeed, many interesting and wholly valid analogies to be drawn. Embryology provides some of the strongest direct evidence there is in favour of the general concept of evolution. But in the first flush of nineteenth-century enthusiasm speculation undoubtedly went much too far in this direction. If a prior theological or philosophical conviction can distort one's appreciation and understanding of natural phenomena, so too can a strongly-held scientific belief. The results of such distortion are always inhibiting, and can hold back progress in the subject for years or decades. Scientists in the late nineteenth century summed up their beliefs about the relationship between evolution and embryology in the phrase 'ontogeny recapitulates phylogeny'. A more popular, that is less technical, expression was that the embryo climbs up its own evolutionary tree during the course of its development. Similar expressions, or at least their implications, are still to be found in popular books and magazine articles. In so far as the general public is aware of anything very much concerning the embryo, these are some of the ideas that seem today to permeate our culture. The most facile arguments were and still are advanced in support of the notion that in its earlier stages of development a human embryo is 'nothing but' a kind of amoeba or a minute mass of vegetable matter; or that later, when it is seen, at about three weeks of development, to have a long thin body (measured, of course, in millimetres only), and is segmented like a worm, that it really is 'nothing but' a worm-like invertebrate. At four and five weeks one sees the so-called 'gill-arches' and 'gill-clefts' that have led superficial observers to conclude that this really is a fish-stage, that human embryos go through a period as fishes swimming in their private intra-uterine pond. Then there is the time when the developing nervous system, and the vertebral column that houses it, outstrip the development of the rest of the trunk. This leads to the transient appearance of a tail on the embryo. It has been argued, then, that this represents a true monkey-stage in human development. So too the appearance of the first-formed body-hair, which is longer than the 'down' to which we are more accustomed, and which is shed before birth normally, has been cited as evidence of a non-human stage in development.

All these facts—and the observed phenomena must be regarded as facts in a strict sense—provide powerful evidence, as mentioned earlier, in support of the general theory of evolution, and of the kinship that undoubtedly exists not only between different races of men, but also between Man and the rest of nature. But simply to conclude that 'ontogeny recapitulates phylogeny' is to ignore another whole empire of scientific knowledge, namely the science of genetics.

We now know enough about heredity, and the way that genetic information is coded in linear fashion on the chromosomes of the nucleus of every cell in our bodies, to be able to state categorically that the recapitulation-theory, in the form it took in the past, was false. That is not to say it was not a useful theory. One of the principal functions of scientific theories is to stimulate thoughtful enquiry, and this the recapitulation-theory certainly did. The element of truth that it contained has been most clearly expounded by Sir Gavin de Beer, whose book *Embryos and Ancestors*[2] finally demolished its nineteenth-century formulation. De Beer concludes that embryos do not successively resemble, and cannot legitimately be homologised with, the *adult* forms of their evolutionary ancestors. But embryos do resemble ancestral *embryonic* forms. This fact can provide many valuable leads in working out phylogenetic relations. But knowledge of genetics precludes our ever stating that an embryo of one species is 'nothing but' an example of some simpler, more primitive form. That cannot be, because the pattern of the chromosomes, which determine the developmental potential, and direct the actual development, of the growing creature, is quite specific and precise. Each one of us inherited, from the time when our mother's egg was fertilised by our father's sperm, not only all our shared characteristics but also many of those that are quite individual, such as the precise colour of our eyes and skin, our fingerprints and the shape of our faces. So far as shared heritable characteristics are concerned, it is because of them that we are members of the genus *Homo* and of the order *Primata*, members of the class *Mammalia* and of the sub-phylum *Vertebrata*. Our shared heredity, because it is the expression of a chemical and physical ordering of matter, makes each one of us a part of, and ought to make us feel at one with, the physical

2. de Beer, Sir Gavin, *Embryos and Ancestors*, O.U.P., 1930; revised edition, 1951.

world from which we have evolved. But each one of us is also a literally unique expression of the world. This uniqueness is the inevitable result not only of a unique genetic background, but also of the specificity of the moulding experiences to which each of us has been subjected, both before and after birth. These are never identical for any two individuals, not even for so-called identical twins. What emerges, finally, from the process of development, is a unique person, and it is person-ality that makes it possible for us to engage in the highest human activity, namely to love.

According to Teilhard's law of complexity-consciousness the history of our world-in-evolution demonstrates beyond peradventure that along the time-axis there have developed both increasing degrees of complexity-in-organisation and, *pari passu*, increasing levels of consciousness. By emphasising (though not, to my mind, often enough) the essential *groping* character of the evolutionary process, he is careful to control what would otherwise be an altogether too optimistic and naive interpretation of the world, many aspects of which must cause us to pause and say, 'but this is biological regress, not progress.' That there is a tendency in evolution towards in-creasing complexity and increasing consciousness seems un-deniable. But that the tendency is sometimes frustrated and side-tracked is equally undeniable. In *Le Milieu Divin* Teilhard uses the word 'diminishments' to describe certain facets of spiritual life. This penetrating expression is worthy of wider use, in other contexts. Study of the pathology as well as of the physiology of natural processes leads one to see 'diminish-ments' in operation in a good many situations besides the adult human one.

It is important to appreciate that embryos suffer such diminishments to a very considerable degree. It has been cal-culated that in man, as is known more definitely to be the case in other mammalian species, the death-rate amongst embryos (and I speak here only of death from 'natural causes') is at least thirty per cent. Most spontaneous abortions, or miscarriages, are probably the result of inborn errors in the make-up of the *conceptus*, many occurring before the fact of pregnancy was established or even seriously suspected. These genetic accidents form part and parcel of the mechanism of evolution, because they are the basis from which natural selection selects. There is increasing evidence also that a variety of environmental factors, again arising from natural causes, can harm the embryo in the womb. To be alive at all is to be at permanent risk. This incredible adventure, on which we all started some nine months before we were born, is fraught with perils at every stage. As the distinguished embryologist George Corner once observed, 'Those of us who survive are truly the elect, chosen from a larger multitude.'[3] Election carries responsibilities, and we do well to remember those whose candidature for survival was unsuccessful.

Now if the human genetic complex, contained at fertilisation within an egg the size of the smallest visible grain of sand, carries all the complex information necessary for the development of an individual to full maturity, is not the egg the most complicated cell of all? Is it right to think of subsequent development in terms of increasing complexity? And if not, what happens to the theory of complexity-consciousness? There is a paradox here, one that is inherent too in the law we are considering, as expounded by Teilhard in terms of evolution. The ultimate end is somehow implied by, and contained within, the beginning. In fact the paradox is even more striking when one reflects that the potential is always wider in scope, and of greater significance, than the actual that is achieved. It seems to me unlikely that, at this early stage of exploration of the law of complexity-consciousness, we shall

3. Corner, G. W., *Ourselves Unborn: an Embryologist's Essay on Man*, Yale University Press, New Haven, 1944.

be in a position to resolve the paradox. I certainly am not. But a brief description, followed by an analogy, may help to direct the thoughts of better philosophers than I along profitable lines.

Embryologists speak of the fertilised ovum as a 'totipotential cell'. After its first cleavage-division the two daughter cells remain 'totipotent': if separated from one another they are likely to give rise to two complete individuals. This is one of the ways in which identical twins arise. If, however, the cells remain united and continue to divide, there arises a small knot of cells we call a 'morula' (literally a 'mulberry'). All these cells are now called 'pluripotent' because, although none of them is capable of giving rise to a whole individual, each is capable of forming any part of the individual-in-the-making it is called upon to make. With further multiplication of cells but continued union, some degree of specialisation becomes inevitable. Teilhard's phrase, applicable here as in many other situations, is 'union differentiates'. Analysis of the ways in which initially identical cells in the embryo gradually specialise, become differentiated, and form the separate tissues and organs of which we are made, is one of the most intriguing aspects of professional embryological research. The complexities that reveal themselves are quite breathtaking in their scope and in their 'audacity'. Some of the first cells to specialise are those that will form no part of the baby after birth. These constitute the 'extra-embryonic tissues and membranes'. They are, in effect, special organs which meet the requirements of the developing embryo for oxygen and carbon-dioxide exchanges, for absorption of foodstuffs and for the elimination of the breakdown products of metabolism. Most remarkably, though, the embryo organises its own environment by means of these extra-corporeal organs. One of their many functions is to elaborate, at a very early stage, complex hormones which act on the mother's body to prevent her having the menstrual period which would normally be expected some two weeks after fertilisation, and which would, of course, be disastrous for the embryo. Moral theologians have committed themselves and the Church to peculiar views at times about the status of these extra-embryonic structures, namely as to whether they are to be regarded as part of the individual or not. Although it is true they are discarded at birth, yet they are as much a part of the total organism *in utero* as are, say, the external gills of larval amphibians which are shed at metamorphosis. From the end of the first week in human embryology they constitute a literally vital part of this unique, developing organism. Subsequent differentiation and specialisation of cells within the embryo itself show equally remarkable fitness and adaptation to the needs of the organism. Sometimes, of course, some necessary complexification falls short of perfection, and the result is congenital disease or death. As we have said, to be alive at all is to be at permanent risk, and the risks are greatest in the early stages. The surprising thing is not that some embryos fail to survive, but rather that so many contrive successfully to negotiate all the hazards through which they must pass.

Consciousness, as we know it in the human individual, would not be possible without this growth and differentiation of specialised cells, tissues and organs. Nor would it be possible without their acting in harmony and unison. When this two-way process is in full operation then the actualisation of potential is maximised.

One can make an analogy at this point with groups of persons constituting a community. Any size of community will serve, from a small family-group upwards. Ultimately our aim must be really to experience the analogy in terms of the whole community of people that constitutes the human race. To illustrate my thesis, though, I will choose a community of intermediate size but of global significance. In my lectures to first-year medical students, I sometimes make the suggestion that they should think of themselves as constituting, as a group, a sort of embryo at the morula-stage, each cell more or less alike, and all of them 'pluripotent'. During their formative years of medical study they will be subjected to a common discipline, but they will also have opportunity to explore the multiple pathways that are open to them in this attractive profession. As time goes on they find themselves, depending on individual interests and abilities, becoming separated out into specialist groups. But however specialised and narrow one becomes he still retains his membership of the profession, and maintains its common purpose—the relief of sickness and suffering. As with the cells of the human body, some of the most important work is carried out by those 'cells' or 'individuals' who specialise in being undifferentiated (if you will excuse the paradox), capable of fulfilling multiple roles, and of assuming a variety of special functions as required. The medical community is world-wide. Whether an individual member is a general surgeon or physician, or a specialist in some minute branch, whether he becomes a medical writer or a general practitioner, a teacher or laboratory scientist, he will always feel at home with fellow-members of the profession in any part of the world. Precisely out of the co-operation that follows from this unity-in-diversity, wholly new insights and advances in treatment are to be expected, and do of course arise, as we are all aware.

This is but one example, at the psycho-social stage of evolution, of the operation of Teilhard's law of complexity-consciousness. Given the potential, the dynamism, and the operation of natural selection in an evolutionary situation, something wholly new is bound to emerge. Each of us, through our personal embryological and post-natal history, represents another example of the operation of this important law. Complexity-consciousness is not only the means by which the world expresses itself in meaningful terms. It is also the means by which each of us acquires and expresses his own personality. It will, if we so choose, provide the key to the future of man and of his relationship to God.

Evolution, Marxism and Christianity: Studies in the Teilhardian Synthesis, ed. B. Towers and A. O. Dyson, Garnstone Press, London, 1967, pp. 47-57.

7

OPTIMISM AND PESSIMISM IN CONTEMPORARY CULTURE

To say that there is a crisis in human affairs is trite. Men have been saying this sort of thing throughout recorded history, whether about their own affairs or those of others. So the expression probably always has been trite. What is peculiar, though, about the present crisis, what makes it at once more stimulating and more alarming than anything that has gone before, is that for the first time in history the problem is total, and this in two senses: first, it is total in the sense of being world-wide, and second, in the sense that it strikes at the very roots of existence for all men. I am not referring simply to the ever-present threat of global atomic warfare, though that is more than enough to produce a crisis-situation in itself. Those of us whose work brings us into continuous contact with the alert minds of the young in universities, are perhaps more conscious than most of the extent to which the sheer reality of the stock-piles of atomic warheads has conditioned their thinking about themselves and about the future. The effect of psychological trauma such as this is sometimes overt, but more often is repressed for the time being. We shall not know the full effects of growing up in this strange new 'total' climate of thought and feeling for many years yet.

But the atom-bomb is only one aspect, a symptom rather than a cause, of the *Angst* experienced by so many today and that underlies the current crisis. To blame the situation, as many have done, on the disillusionment created by two world wars, then simply to hope that things will come right if we can only avoid another conflagration in this century, is to analyse at altogether too superficial a level. Optimism and pessimism are born of deeper things. After all, one can fight a war, even accept defeat and death, and remain at heart optimistic: if not for oneself, at least for one's companions or even for one's conquerors. But when even the victors themselves, the successful ones, are pessimistic, what then?

It can, of course, be said with justice that people tend naturally to fall into the one category or the other, optimist or pessimist. Such personality-traits, resulting from influences both of heredity and of early childhood experiences, tend to persist throughout life. They are self-reinforcing, in that an identical stimulus will tend to evoke from two different people the response appropriate to his personality. The response will be 'facilitated', or 'reinforced' as physiologists say, with each experience of the stimulus. It has often been observed that if the two types are presented with some desirable commodity in a container large enough to hold twice the quantity offered, the one will recognise it as 'half-full' while the other will see it as 'half-empty'. Both views of course are correct. They represent, however, a basically positive and a basically negative response to life.

It seems to me true that the negative response is the more characteristic of much of recent Western culture. Waves of pessimism, cynicism, and ultra-sophisticated despair have swept across our theatres and other media of communication. It is unlikely to be the case that writers ever actually have the power to create the public attitudes that bring them popularity and success. The creative artist reflects and expresses a *Weltanschauung* which may or may not be popular at the moment. His work will be commercially successful in so far as his views, compounded of his experiences and their expression, mirror those of the general public. He is successful, then, in so far as he gives the public what it wants or thinks it wants, or some kind of imitation of this. Once a successful formula has been found, of course, there is never any shortage of pseudo-artists and entrepreneurs to exploit the advantages of the moment. There can be little doubt that 'sick' pessimism has been an extraordinary commercial success during the last twenty years. When one speaks, therefore, of 'waves of pessimism', one does not wish to imply that we are on the point of being engulfed: waves express commercial fashions, and are never permanent. What is more interesting about a wave is its first-felt swell, and what contributed to its growth and development. What lies behind the public response? Why have pessimists had such a good time of it (if the expression is not too paradoxical) in recent years?

Some intellectuals, and other sophisticated manipulators of public opinion, together with many members of the general public themselves, seem somehow to have lost their grip on life during the last few decades. Many of us seem to be suffering from the sort of *malaise* that is characteristic of a certain type of patient who finally discovers, or dimly discerns, that what he thought was a temporary indisposition is in fact a terminal illness, that is, one to which the expected outcome, in the readily-discernible future, is death. Specific reactions to this confrontation are very varied. They have provided themes for any number of 'romantic' books. Modern romance explores individual attitudes and responses in depth, being one of the later expressions of the post-Renaissance cult of the individual. But whether fear or apparent nonchalance, paralysis of will or a determination to squeeze the last drop out of the orange (or should one say 'lemon'?) of life, whether railing or resignation dominates the observed reactions, they all stem from the sheer inescapability of the underlying fact that time is perceived to be running out: the individual's human life, as hitherto known and experienced, is about to come to an end. *Timor mortis conturbat me.* This 'disturbance' may finally induce a kind of stoical resignation, seen not infrequently in the modern atheistic existentialist, for whom death is the ultimate absurdity of a recognisably absurd life. Whatever the personal 'solution' that the individual may adopt towards his predicament, the underlying mood these days is all too often one of cynicism and despair, a fundamental pessimism from which it is difficult to be distracted for long. Behind these manifestations there lies a feeling of terrible boredom with life: one cannot but be bored with something that has no future.

There is nothing new, it may justly be said, in this analogy from individual experience. The effects are the inevitable result of the continuance of one half of a powerful christian tradition, associated with the jettisoning of the other half by means of which that tradition appeared humanly tolerable. Christians have spoken of the world for so long as a 'vale of tears', that they can hardly complain if some non-christian contemporaries take the expression literally, and feel depressed and pessimistic as a result. Christianity, of course, has its own optimism and glory. But the traditional optimism of the christian 'solution', summed up so devastatingly but with consummate skill and accuracy in the phrase 'pie in the sky', is regarded today as wholly unacceptable. A return to that mode of thinking and feeling, no matter how cleverly it might be presented, offers no hope for the modern dilemma. That kind of christian message may still act as a palliative for a diminishing few. Palliatives, if they pretend to be other than what they are, are cheats. And if they do not make that pretence, then their effectiveness as palliatives is grossly curtailed. Cheating is one of the things that the modern so-called amoral conscience repudiates—unless it be as a temporary measure, designed and agreed on as a technique for the handling of absurdity, nonsense and boredom. Out of all the pain and suffering of twentieth-century experience has come an urgent demand for honesty, integrity, and truth. Herein might lie some ground for optimism, if only the modern concept of the absurdity of things did not make these concepts absurd in their turn.

The roots of the current human dilemma and human crisis lie, as all roots necessarily do, in history. Christianity is *par excellence* an historical religion: not simply because of the historical Christ, but also because of its historical need to preserve the deposit of faith, to defend orthodoxy and resist those passing winds of fashion that would dilute, modify and eventually overthrow its divinely-inspired teaching, with its massive exploration in depth over the centuries. The failure of orthodox christianity to communicate effectively to more than a very small fraction of those moderns who are knowledgeable, sensitive and 'aware', can itself be a source of sorrow to those who look back with a certain nostalgia on the days of faith. They find, though, that the traditional, escapist optimism of the Church, is no longer effective to relieve the pain. Christians once were the salt of the earth. But what when the salt loses its flavour?

No one has been more conscious than Teilhard de Chardin of the reality and urgency of the problem facing mankind in this century. No one saw more clearly the general direction in which the solution must lie. No one has argued a case more passionately, more brilliantly, and on the whole more successfully. His work will eventually be seen to constitute a watershed in the history of the Church and the history of the world. In an inadequate analogy from art-history he might be compared to one of the founders of Impressionism. The analogy is valid, perhaps, not only in respect of the work itself, but also in the criticism it has had to endure. Impressionism, for all the early complaints of its lack of clarity and form, and for all its real limitations, unquestionably marked one of the most significant watersheds in the history of painting. Above all, it offered hope for advance at a time when traditional techniques had been exploited to the point of standstill. This is what Teilhard does on a much broader canvas: we may look now with anticipation for further exploration of the new medium, and for development from it. There is hope in Teilhard. Is this simply because he himself had those basic characteristics of an optimist? Are his conclusions justified by the evidence, or is he just another victim of self-delusion?

There are some facts about the christian position in the contemporary 'post'-christian culture that we do well to bear in mind. Firstly, christian dogma has been elaborated, ever since the Church was founded, by men whose understanding of the world was couched entirely in static, 'fixist' or (which comes to the same thing in the end) cyclical terms. There is no fault or blame to be attached to this: it is simply a fact which must be accepted and taken into account. Secondly, the move-ment within christianity that tends to despise the world in preference for other-worldliness has, despite its periodical condemnation as heretical, always had a fatal attraction for earnest members of the Church, and has exercised an influence in ecclesiastical circles that at times has almost encompassed the ruin of major elements in the deposit of faith. Thirdly, the discovery that the world is not a static or cyclical affair, but is in evolution at every moment and in every phase of its activity, is of very recent origin. Modern man 'knows' that this discovery is true. Those who cling to earlier formulations, and restrict themselves to terms that are appropriate only in a static or cyclical world, automatically eliminate themselves from the possibility of fruitful dialogue with modern man. It will be said of this that it is altogether too strong a statement. I do not believe that to be so. There are still those in the Church, in high positions, who are prepared to speak dis-paragingly of evolution as 'only a theory', and to imply that it is as likely as not a false one. There must be countless numbers amongst the faithful who are only too relieved to follow them and stick to older modes of thinking. They are all, in my view, whistling in the dark, in order to bolster up an outlook about natural phenomena now known to be false—at least, the static or cyclical view is known to be false over a period of some thousands of millions of years. The dangers inherent in 'the forces of reaction' are immense. The Church simply cannot afford another episode like that of Galileo.

The difficulties that theologians clearly find in dealing at all adequately with the concept of evolution stem partly from their lack of 'feeling' for its reality. If it is true that 'there is nothing in the intellect which is not first in the senses', then the only adequate preparation for the handling of scientific concepts is practical science itself. If this is thought to be too demanding, one can only reply that worth-while academic studies *are* demanding. Theologians are in no way exempt from the ordinary rules for the acquisition of scientific knowledge. They are not gifted with extraordinary insight into natural phenomena. But of course the non-scientists or anti-scientists are not the only ones to share the blame for non-communication. Major problems stem from the history of biological evolution itself. The anti-religious bias and purpose of many of its early promoters inevitably provoked reaction. But it should be remembered in this context that attempts to 'reduce man to the level of the beasts' (to use a phrase that might have come equally well from the pen of a nineteenth-century materialist scientist or a twentieth-century 'immaterialist' spiritual writer) would have been wholly without effect if it had not been for the strong manichean element in both groups. Put very simply, the question is whether or not one finds the beasts 'beastly'. Does it induce feelings of nausea and repugnance, or rather of pride and exhilaration, to realise and accept that every cell of one's body has a direct physical link, through countless millions of subhuman forms, with 'base' matter? The question is one of respect for things. It seems to me that it is a lack of respect on all sides that lies behind much of the current social malaise.

The crisis for modern man has arisen from his inability to recognise the world and its contents as good and wholesome. After its denigration for spiritual ends came the scientific era, when those same assessments were taken to their logical conclusions. To the average person today the world really is no more than a minute planet, wandering in space with an ultimately bleak and empty future. On it, owing to wholly fortuitous circumstances, certain energies have been temporarily trapped, and have produced many weird and wonderful effects. But none of them *mean* anything, nor can do so in principle. Man himself is part of this game of chance. Though he may be on the crest of an evolutionary wave for the moment he will inevitably go the way of all biological species, namely to extinction. It is absurd to try to console oneself with the reflection that the species might survive for a long time yet. What difference does it make if ten generations lie ahead or ten thousand, if in the long run there is nothing but decay and desolation? Only two responses might seem appropriate, and they are not new to mankind: either *carpe diem*, that is to enjoy the moment by exploiting all the distractions currently available, or to commit suicide. Mankind desperately needs a more worthy philosophy.

Teilhard had the courage to accept an evolving world, and the ability and enthusiasm to think out its implications according to evidence currently available from all sides of human experience. His interpretations allow for the greatest reconciliation and resolution of conflict ever known in the world's history. His key concepts of tangential and radial energy, of cosmogenesis culminating in christogenesis, his law of complexity-consciousness as the underlying 'drive' of evolution-in-action, all these and many other insights will, if they are properly explored, and properly expounded, give back to man, in a context he can fully accept, that sense of worthwhileness, of personal dignity and purpose, without which he cannot recover from his current neurosis. Widespread pessimism is a sign of widespread neurosis. It is now possible, with Teilhard, to see the start of recovery from illness. It will doubtless be slow, sometimes painful, and there will be many setbacks. But an optimism of being, and not simply an optimism of escape, is now once again possible. Do we dare be pessimistic about a world which God so loved that he immersed himself in it at the incarnation?

Pax Romana Journal, 1967, pp. 20-22.

8

A DECADE OF TEILHARD

1. REVIEW-ARTICLE, 1958

The works of Teilhard de Chardin, now being published posthumously, appear to be having a considerable impact on certain sections of the Catholic community on the Continent. The time is hardly ripe yet for the publication of a full critical appraisal of his writings, and the author of this book[1] would not pretend that it is more than an introduction to Teilhard himself, with an exposition of certain features of his writings which appear particularly to call for critical comment. More important at this stage than commentaries, is that the works themselves should be read and talked about. Slowly, then, by constant usage, we shall extract more and more meaning out of those brilliant new words and phrases that Teilhard has introduced into the study of the history of the world: words such as *enroulement*, to describe the essential feature of the evolutionary process (compare the traditional *déroulement*); and *hominisation*, to indicate the unquestioned tendency in evolution, especially in the vertebrates, for increasing elaboration of the central nervous system without which, so far as we can see, those characteristics which we recognise as essentially human would not be possible. *Hominisation* becomes, then, the end of the evolutionary process, for it is admitted by not a few biologists today that of all the species now extant, it is *Homo*

1. Rabut o.p., Olivier A., *Dialogue Avec Teilhard De Chardin* (Editions du Cerf, Paris). English translation subsequently published by Sheed and Ward, London, 1961.

sapiens alone which is capable of making any further *major* evolutionary advance. This is attributed by Teilhard precisely to Man's spiritual capacities, by virtue of which, in continuation of the process of *enroulement*, he is offered the possibility (one species representing all the rest) of discovering at the heart of all creation the Omega, present there from the beginning as the Alpha. In this way we can look to the fulfilment, in Teilhard's view, of St Paul's hope that 'nature in its turn will be set free from the tyranny of corruption, to share in the glorious freedom of God's sons.'

Visions such as these, word-pictures painted on a time-scale canvas of thousands of millions of years, with the speed and the tensions mounting continually to new heights of awareness and self-awareness and the liberation thus achieved, are exciting indeed. What a book is waiting, one hopes, some day to be produced, which will compare Teilhard's concept of *enroulement* in phylogenetic development, with Jung's *individuation* as the proper end of ontogeny! We may have to wait a long time for such a book in this country. For Teilhard is virtually unknown here. Not one of his works has appeared thus far (1958) in English translation, and since Teilhard was as much a poet and mystic as he was a man of science, it requires a great delicacy of feeling for the French language to follow all the subtleties of his thought in the original.

Perhaps some publisher could be persuaded to make a start for English readers with a translation of Père Rabut's book. British scientists, steeped in the empirical tradition, might find a certain lack of appeal in the more lyrical passages of Teilhard's own writings—though it is to be noted that the scientific committee which is partly responsible for these posthumous publications includes a number of the most distinguished British and American biologists. But the most empirical of scientists would find an ally in Père Rabut. In the first section of his book he makes the grievous charge of a lack of objectivity in Teilhard's scientific assessment of the evolutionary process, and contrasts the certain inevitability which he invokes with the accounts of evolutionary theorists like G. G. Simpson, who stress rather the fundamental randomness of the factors involved in evolutionary advance. Teilhard does indeed sometimes appear to hold views which would be unacceptable to thorough-going neo-Darwinians of today. It is refreshing to see his views challenged from this point of view in a book which carries the triple *nihil obstat, imprimi potest*, and *imprimatur*.

But Teilhard would not, one imagines, be daunted by the charge. He tends in fact not to discuss the mechanisms involved in the origin of species, nor the laws which govern those mechanisms. A palaeontologist of world-wide reputation, his standpoint is that of the historian, not that of the experimentalist. The history of evolution, presented by Teilhard with the strict objectivity that his scientific training demanded, leads most compellingly to his conclusion that, whatever may have been the precise factors operating at each stage of the process, the net result has been the increasing elaboration of complex organisation (the very reverse of the law of increasing entropy), a process which has led in turn from what he calls the geosphere, through the biosphere, finally to the noosphere as realised in Man. It should perhaps be stated unequivocally that for Teilhard the advent of the noosphere is a transformation so revolutionary that he is prepared to allow for it (e.g. in footnote, p. 186, *Le Phénomène Humain*) whatever 'creative act' or 'special intervention' anyone might wish to postulate. He himself would probably prefer to see this as yet another, special, manifestation of that divine Power which he sees displayed everywhere throughout the created universe. His is the view, in essence mystical, that was described by the late Dr Sherwood Taylor in *The Fourfold Vision* as 'essentially religious, though not essentially

Christian . . . the vision of the whole universe, down to the moss and the stone, as the consequence of God's will and as actively fulfilling his purpose.' This vision which, as Père Rabut points out, probably came to Teilhard not as the result of his scientific work (as sometimes he seems to imply) but intuitively when he was a boy, does become for him essentially christian in the light of the modern development, in ever fuller measure, of the doctrine of the Incarnation. For Teilhard, the evolutionary process will achieve its final term only when the Christus Rex is acknowledged by the whole human race— acknowledged not separately by individuals seeking private salvation, but acknowledged in unison by the whole species, members one of another, praising God in that full freedom which is theirs uniquely, and doing so on behalf of the whole biosphere and geosphere through which Man has come to be.

The *Dialogue* under review is well-named. Though the author is critical of many aspects of Teilhard's writings, yet he quotes freely from them, often in order to show how brilliantly on occasion there is expressed a theological truth of the utmost significance. A reading of this book gives one a fair insight into Teilhard's thoughts and methods. It is a valuable introduction, and has the advantage of providing at the same time a useful criticism of the defects and omissions which can be charged against his grand synthesis. One of the gravest accusations is his almost total neglect of the problem of evil.[2] The charge was anticipated in an appendix to the first book published, but the answer to it, as given there, is curiously naive. Père Rabut repeatedly gives evidence of a certain naivety in philosophical matters. But his positive achievements are regarded as of the utmost significance. Provided that the point is made, as in this book it is but not sufficiently in the original writings, that with the advent of the noosphere

2. But see above, page 52.

the inevitability of the biological process of evolution is pro-gressively overshadowed by the freedom of self-conscient man either to co-operate with the grace and opportunities now offered him or to refuse them, Teilhard's synthesis will be seen in time to be of the very first importance. The techno-logical advances of modern man might legitimately be thought of as the further extension of a purely biological process, and as such inevitable. Spiritual advance, though, is totally distinct from this. Although one might hope and pray that such advance will be the final destiny of Man, we only delude our-selves if we imagine, as perhaps some of Teilhard's followers have been tempted to do, that there is anything inevitable about it. The final choice is in fact becoming increasingly well-defined. Thinking people everywhere seem to be con-scious of an approaching crisis. Let us hope that Teilhard is right, and that it is unthinkable that in this last crisis, when the process of *enroulement* has almost achieved the goal pursued for some three thousand million years, men will choose to destroy it all. Will the final victory lie with God or with the devil? Teilhard was an incorrigible optimist in questions such as that.

The synoptic views of Teilhard are here shown to be strikingly in sympathy with the general spirit of the post-war world. There is a great movement going on towards synthesis and union in all kinds of fields, social, political, intellectual and spiritual. It will not be surprising if Teilhard's voice is heard repeatedly, and more and more forcefully, in the next few generations. He combines, as both scientist and mystic, the Western obsession with the Manifold in all degrees of particularity, with the Eastern vision of the One. Always he talks in terms of history, but it is history on a time-scale almost inconceivable by those of us who are conditioned to think of 'Ancient History' in terms of Greeks and Romans. Arts men, scientists, theologians and philosophers, none will be able to afford to neglect the fact of Teilhard de Chardin.

Blackfriars, 1959, vol. 40, pp. 126-9.

2. ADDRESS IN THE SERIES 'MAN IN EVOLUTION', ST JOHN'S COLLEGE, CAMBRIDGE, 1967

Pierre Teilhard de Chardin was a Christian priest of rare spiritual insight, and was also a scientist of great eminence. His geological and palaeontological studies, published in the journals of learned societies in Europe, Asia and America, constitute the kind of lasting contribution to science that marks a distinguished scholar. The honours which he received from, and the esteem in which he was held by, his scientific colleagues are matters of record. But he was not only a highly skilled and dedicated research worker, whose labours served to push forward the boundaries of knowledge 'inch by inch'. This is the normal way in which science advances, by the steady, competent work of those who have mastered the necessary skills. But as well as being a master in his scientific field, he was also one of those relatively rare people, a pioneer of science. He was, in fact, a pioneer of great intellectual daring and originality, whose ideas are likely to modify profoundly, and to advance enormously, our understanding of the nature of science and of its relation to other aspects of living.

The concepts that he developed on the basis of his *experience* of both the scientific and the religious life, offer in particular the hope of a solution to the centuries-old conflict between science and religion. This conflict has shown itself in a variety of ways: either in open warfare, or armed neutrality, or mutually suspicious disdain. Even indifference, as psychologists well know, is often a form of aggression. Teilhard's approach to the problem of Science and Faith is in no sense a search for the 'highest common factor' in the traditional thinking of each side. Rather it is like the sudden growth in a plant of a leading shoot, which draws into itself all that is of value from the roots and stem that support it, and then creates, out of the labour of growth, a structure that determines the direction along which subsequent development will proceed.

The use of the language of growth and development is deliberate. Teilhard's scientific studies convinced him beyond all doubting that, just as an individual is in a continuous state of dynamic interaction with his environment, so too, in the evolutionary process, are individual species and other, larger, taxonomic groups. Evolution, Teilhard says, is 'a general condition to which all theories, all hypotheses, all systems must bow, and which they must satisfy henceforward if they are to be thinkable and true. Evolution is a light illuminating all facts, a curve that all lines must follow.'

As yet the science of evolution is only in its infancy. In scientific circles there is no longer any debate as to whether or not man is a product of an evolutionary process. But there is a great deal of debate as to how that process operates; whether it shows 'direction' or is entirely haphazard; and, in view of the apparently unpredictable, chance nature of many of its operations, whether or not there can be detected any 'meaning' in the evolutionary process. A very powerful intellectual current that has been running through Western European (and especially British) scientific and philosophical thinking for three generations or more, has sought to persuade us that meaningfulness is non-existent in nature, that the only 'meaning' that can be detected is something like the internal consistency of, say, a puzzle or a game where, provided one sticks to the humanly-imposed rules and carries them out logically, there is a chance that a pattern and a 'solution' will emerge. But it is meaningless to ask about the inner significance of the puzzle as a whole, because it really has no meaning, being merely a form of diversion. The 'success' of this movement of human and cosmic denigration is well recognised in the popularity of certain types of modern book- and play-writing.

We see here the final bankruptcy of traditional modes of thinking about the world, all of which have looked on it as something essentially static or at the most cyclical (which comes, in the end, to mean the same thing as static). Many professed evolutionists are still the victims of inherited modes of thinking. They regard the process of evolution itself as no more than a crazy merry-go-round, one of great complexity of course, but one in which nothing really meaningful ever emerges. These conclusions are mostly conditioned by nineteenth-century theories in classical physics, which suggested that if there were any 'direction' in the cosmos it must necessarily be towards disintegration and increased randomness in organisation. Apparent progress, then, in any part of the process of biological evolution, becomes no more than a swirl or eddy in a stream that leads inevitably to decay, disintegration, and the coldness of death. If there is no meaning at the cosmic level it isn't easy for a man to find meaning in his own life and in his own most certain death.

Teilhard, the expert palaeontologist, takes us back through time in order to give us a glimpse into the future. His approach is always that of the scientist, one who experiences phenomena-in-themselves (whether physical, biological or spiritual), and who speaks from this ground of experience. His greatest single contribution to science will probably be his 'law of complexity-consciousness'. This law expresses a truth about nature quite as profound as, and in some ways more significant than, those expressed by the established laws of thermodynamics, to which we have referred. Throughout evolutionary time we can see, according to Teilhard (and of course he was not the first to see what in fact is fairly obvious), that the matter or stuff of the universe organises itself into an ever-increasing complex of interrelated component-parts. He goes on to say that this observed process makes manifest a property of matter which is more fundamental and more meaningful than anything observed before in science. With increase in complexity, not only of individual organisms, but also of the group to which they belong and indeed the 'system' out of which they have evolved, there has been a corresponding rise in the psychic quality of life until, with Man, we see not only some degree of conscious control of the material world, but also the *possibility* at least of the psychic becoming increasingly spiritualised, and of the spiritual finally taking precedence: its failure so to do represents the state of 'original sin', a state from which, by the merits of Christ, mankind can be redeemed.

Teilhard sees his law, like the Second Law of Thermodynamics of which it forms a sort of counterpart, as acting like a current which draws all things ultimately in the one direction. But again, of course, as in any stream, there are eddies and swirls in the flow. At any point one may see a reversal in operation. But, says Teilhard, if one looks long enough and over a wide-enough area, it becomes obvious that in the system as a whole there is a steady increase in complexity-consciousness.

He coined the term 'radial energy' to express this increase in degree of interiority or consciousness, and contrasted this with the 'outwardly-turning' forces with which scientists are more accustomed to deal, all of which he grouped together under the term 'tangential energy'. Scientists who have been struck by the usefulness of these new expressions are beginning to think out ways of measuring levels of consciousness or radial energy. It is only when things can be expressed quantitatively that they are really capable of being handled scientifically.

Teilhard coined other words too. We are used to speaking

of the composition of the inorganic world in terms of litho-sphere (for the solid crust), hydrosphere (for the watery layer on the surface) and atmosphere (for the gaseous 'envelope' that surrounds us). Earlier this century the word 'biosphere' came into use to denote the 'layer' of living creatures that covers the surface of the earth. With the advent of self-reflecting man, says Teilhard, another term is needed, to denote the 'mind-layer' or nexus of ideas that covers the earth, now all the more densely because of the development of modern communi-cations-systems. For this mind-layer he used the word 'noosphere'. At this stage evolution shows itself as primarily convergent rather than divergent. And so, following logically a process which he sees as leading eventually to what he calls 'Omega-point' (when 'God shall be all-in-all', in the words of St Paul), he develops the theme of the 'christosphere'. To fur-ther the development of this last stage of the evolutionary process is a special task of the christian church and of each of its members. But this can not be done in isolation from the rest of the process. And thus we see that study of the natural sciences is as much a part of the work of redemption, of the task of creating the mystical body of Christ, as are some of the more conventional and more strictly spiritual exercises.

Teilhard's ideas, for all their initial strangeness, are thorough-ly orthodox in the sense of being rooted in scripture. By this one does not mean that he merely read into nature the things he 'knew' from sources of revelation. He always had profound respect for the scientific method of study. He always enquired first (and pursued the enquiry with great concentra-tion on detail), 'what are the phenomena?' He subsequently 'saw' that the phenomena, taken from a wide range of discip-lines, could be organised into a great synthesis, one in the midst of which 'meaning' became not only possible but became clearly manifest. People sometimes talk of Teilhard's 'vision' in the super-natural connotation of that much-abused word. But his was 'vision' in its most ordinary, commonsense meaning. Because he 'saw' phenomena as such, and elaborated ideas which are testable by scientific techniques, he built his house on rock, not sand. No doubt many of his hypotheses will be modified as a result of further study and reflection. In the volume of his collected works entitled *The Vision of the Past*[3] he says of scientific hypotheses that they are 'like life, changeable, fragile but progressive. Good hypotheses are continually modified but in a definite direction, by following which they perfect themselves; and at the end of this evolution they attain the rank of fixed elements, destined to figure thereafter in any representation of the world.'

There is no 'Teilhard canon', and we must discourage all attempts to establish one. His ideas must be allowed to work and grow from below, and not be declared, declaimed or otherwise imposed as some kind of authority from above. About his own hypotheses, Teilhard had the outlook of the true scientist. Thus in a lecture given in Pekin in 1942, shortly after he had finished writing *The Phenomenon of Man*, he said: 'The views that I present are still, as I said, only at their birth. Do not therefore take them as universally accepted or definitive. What I am putting before you are suggestions, rather than affirmations. My principal objective is not to convert you to ideas which are still fluid, but to open horizons for you, to make you think.'

As time goes on Teilhard's ideas, for the most part published posthumously, are stimulating millions of people to think. The results, one hopes, can do nothing but good. He is also leading millions of people to pray, or to pray more intently and with greater purpose. He has restored to science, and to the world in general, a sense of direction. Without such a

3. Collins, London, 1966.

sense the human spirit tends to wander aimlessly in pursuit of mere diversion. After Teilhard, one can see the opportunity offered to Man to make a great move forward along the evolutionary curve that is bringing him to convergence on himself and also to convergence on God.

Expository Times, 1968, vol. 79, pp. 276-8.

SECTION TWO

ESSAYS IN
INTERPRETATION AND
COMMUNICATION

I

LIBERAL AND VOCATIONAL
EDUCATION IN THE UNIVERSITY

A paper read to the Catholic University Teachers Conference, 1960

It is a provocative title that the organising committee has given me. Perhaps it was thought that if, as one hopes will happen, sharp differences of opinion are to emerge in this conference, then a conflict such as may be thought to be suggested in the wording of this title might be just the thing to get us off to a good start. If this is what the organisers intended, they were thinking, perhaps, of those hardy perennials, arts versus science or pure science versus technology.

'Liberal' and 'vocational' are words so highly charged with emotional overtones that for some, perhaps, they could almost be described as 'value-judgement words', one good, one bad. Which would be which would depend, probably, on the nature of one's own personal education. He is a bold man and a rare one who will frankly and honestly admit (whatever he may say in jest) that his own education was woefully inadequate.

There is something very fine about the word 'liberal'. A noble word, with a noble etymology. But words are strange things. What they really mean is often largely determined by unconscious appreciation of the meaning of their opposites. And if 'liberal' carries with it an air of freedom, expansiveness and good breeding, how can we fail sharply to react to its opposite, 'illiberal'? This is a word even more highly evocative of emotion. It is difficult to contemplate the nature of 'liberal education' without wanting to contrast it with something we must dislike intensely: illiberal education. Do our minds leap, then, to 'vocational education'? To visions of vast laboratories devoted to ever more specialised branches of science and engineering? To the young people in them desperately cramming in order to make sure of a safe niche for themselves in an ever more complex world of technology? They too must have a sort of 'vocation', I suppose, though it is hard to imagine what kind and quality of 'voice' it could have been that called them. Or is it, for many of them, simply a question of some sort of a job with a reasonably secure future: not in any sense a true calling?

The word 'vocational' has, of course, at least as respectable an etymology as 'liberal'. Not all vocations, not even the majority of them, are pursued mainly for monetary gain and personal profit. It would be absurd to think of most vocations as fundamentally illiberal in nature. Music, architecture, the law, writing, engineering, medicine, the church, academic life itself? All of these, and many others, are properly called vocations. The successful practice of any one of them requires special knowledge and special skills acquired only through education devoted in part precisely to their acquisition. Traditionally such education, or part of it, has been found in the universities. Will anyone say that any one of these vocations is illiberal in itself, no matter how illiberal he might think are individual practitioners of his acquaintance?

I am forced to conclude that no antithesis is implied, nor I hope was intended by the organisers, in the choice of a title for this opening session. After all they could have said 'liberal *or* vocational education in the university', or even, in the style of some examination papers, *and/or*. For myself may I say that I am grateful for that little word 'and'? It is the most valuable word in our language, and quite the most significant. A word that joins things together and makes a whole out of what was disparate and at odds. There is no more important or urgent task set before each of the thousands of different factions into which the human race is divided than to see the unity that underlies all our separateness from one another, from other living creatures, from all creation. Differences in every sphere are, of course, essential, vital. I am not going to plead for uniformity in education or indeed in anything. That would be impossible even if it were desirable. And it is certainly not desirable. But what I *shall* urge is that we should cultivate a growing realisation that differences between groups of men, whether in the small milieu of the university or in the larger one of international affairs, are never really fundamental, since beneath the surface layer of argument and conflict, there are immense depths of being throughout which we find ourselves at one. Every new bud on a tree is significant and of value, in some respects unique. But it can remain so only as long as it retains its organic continuity here and now with the parent stem. This means retaining organic continuity with the past too. We in the universities must first of all realise that, however diverse might be our subjects of research and teaching, we are very much more like one another than we are different. We must learn to see those who belong to the academic community, senior and junior, as members precisely of a community with all that that splendid word implies. Having seen and really experienced the tree as a whole we shall be so much more aware of the real significance of our own branch, our own twig. It is here, at the periphery of the tree, that we experience year by year those leaves through which we breathe the fresh air of young undergraduate thought, and the flowers and fruit of further knowledge and understanding.

The sense of academic community has had a difficult job to survive in recent decades. The reasons are many, and mostly obvious. It is often assumed that the older universities are much better placed to preserve the sense of community than are the more modern foundations. It is clear that in many ways this is so, because the senior members of each college in an ancient university house, teach, entertain and generally care for a group of young people who ideally represent an academic cross-section of the total membership of the university. Social and academic contact between senior and junior members of the college is frequent and close, provided that the senior members appreciate their responsibilities in these matters, and provided that each new junior member of the society is made aware of the opportunities afforded him for enlarging his range of academic experience far beyond that of the particular field of study which he has chosen to pursue. The simple fact of being resident for three years in a college where this sort of thing is possible should provide in itself something of a liberal education, however narrow might be the strictly vocational interests of the student.

It should perhaps be said at this point that there are very few young men (more, proportionately, of young women perhaps) who come up these days in pursuit of a 'liberal education' with no particular end in view. That is possible only in a community where families have means large enough to allow their children to grow up blissfully unaware of the need to earn money. Hardly anyone today can hope to go through life without having to earn part, at least, of his keep. This is a fact that is still, I think, sometimes overlooked by some of us. I remember a Fellow of the Royal Society once saying to me that his branch of science, and the way he taught it, would fit no one for any kind of job. Except, presumably, his own. This was in a discussion on syllabuses and examinations, and was said in the form of a boast. He wanted to point the moral of the 'purity' of his subject compared with other branches of biology, such as my own which is orientated specifically towards the medical profession. Now I applaud the existence of 'useless' subjects in the universities; but I applaud it only to deny it. No intellectual exercise, properly undertaken, is useless, no more than any physical exercise, properly undertaken, can be useless to an athlete no matter what his particular branch of sport might be. One approves the track-exercises of, say, a high-jumper, but it would be absurd to decry either by implication, or even, as happens sometimes in the academic analogy, directly, the exercise he undertakes with the bar itself. The fact that he does the latter with a direct end in view can in no way detract from the value of the work itself, and might even be thought to enhance it.

Most modern undergraduates, then, look upon their period in the university as a preparation for making a living of some sort. In this way practically all courses offered today become vocational. True, a man reading history or English, if he does not intend to enter academic life or become a teacher, may not know precisely what sort of job he will eventually want to do. But whatever it is, whether writing memoranda in industry or the civil service, working with newspapers, radio or television, management in the broad sense, or whatever, his ability to earn money will in part depend on what technical skill he has acquired in the manipulation of words and ideas. Is it 'liberal' to be skilful in manipulating words, and 'illiberal' to be skilful in manipulating the formulae of mathematics, chemistry or physics? How could one possibly judge? But what one can say is that the modern scientist or engineer is more likely to have some familiarity with some of the skills of his colleagues on the arts side than vice versa. If ignorance of and lack of sympathy with vast areas of modern knowledge is a mark of intellectual illiberalism, then it is perhaps the historians and linguists who by and large should look to it most earnestly.

An analysis of these matters was given us recently by Sir Charles Snow in his Rede lecture entitled 'The Two Cultures and the Scientific Revolution'. His topic is one that has been exercising the minds of many educators during recent years.

The problem is that of the very serious lack of communication, in this country, between the self-styled 'intellectuals' in their self-styled 'liberal' arts tradition on the one hand, and the scientists on the other. It is significant that Snow's personal experience of the academic life is that of a Cambridge college, where, as stressed earlier in this paper, conditions are optimal for cultural and intellectual exchange.

There is undoubtedly something very wrong. The fact has been recognised for long enough, and attempts have been made in many universities to correct the situation. How many optional courses have not been provided for members of science faculties on 'Shakespeare', 'Medieval and Renaissance Literature', 'History of Art', and so on? In recent years in Cambridge the reverse has also been tried, and halls packed with arts men have heard courses given by distinguished scientists on 'Why physics?', 'The Chemistry of Life', and so on. There has even been proposed in Cambridge a combined arts-science tripos, designed mainly for the arts man who wants to gain enough appreciation of the scientific method to make his contribution to political and industrial life more effective than it could otherwise possibly be in this scientific era.

In my view all schemes such as these, however praiseworthy their objects, are ill-conceived. They can only begin and end by patching up a mess which should never have been there in the first place. They have the added danger that by giving the impression that something really is being done about the mess they will perpetuate it for that vast number of undergraduates who will never be persuaded, ought never to be beguiled, into taking these so-called liberalising courses of study.

It is no part of the proper function of a university to provide elementary instruction in physics and chemistry, any more than to teach the multiplication tables or the rudiments of literary appreciation. Specialised courses in subjects of which the undergraduate has no previous direct experience are of course an essential part of academic life. But if a man presents himself for instruction in Tibetan it will be safely assumed that he is linguistically prepared for it, just as a man who wants to study high-polymer chemistry will need an extensive background of general chemical knowledge. Rapid progress can then be expected, and the principal ideal which should inspire all university teaching is maintained. This is to teach a man, so far as time allows, up to the furthest limits of his native intellectual capacity, in some cases as far as the point where the pupil outstrips the teacher, whether in 'explicit' knowledge or in his voyage into the unknown on the sea of research. We shall fail in our duty to safeguard our academic heritage if we are prepared to allow university teachers to spend their time trying to make good gross deficiencies in general education, which are the outcome of a schools policy itself dictated by the universities, dictated by the unbalanced requirements for entry into the various faculties.

The responsibility rests squarely with us in the universities. If we require a man to be already a specialist in physics, in French or in classics before he comes up, and so highly skilled a specialist that he must have devoted the greater part of his time in his most formative years (from the academically-educative point of view) to his specialist subjects, we have no right then to deplore the narrowness of his outlook. We ourselves have determined that it should be so.

We hear a lot, in other contexts, about 'deprived children'. If a child is deprived of something essential to its physical growth, or something essential to its educational and psychological growth, it may carry the scars of such privation throughout life unless extensive remedial treatment is undertaken. I look on many of our modern undergraduates, as on ourselves, their teachers, who were undergraduates not so very long ago, as intellectually deprived. Growth to mental maturity ought to follow that pattern of biological development that we see in embryological and post-natal growth, one which we can discern too in the phylogenetic development of Man. Here there is no sudden, early specialisation of one part to the detriment of the rest. Instead a most remarkably gener-alised structure persists right through until very late stages. This is paralleled in psychological development by the need positively felt in the first half of a man's life span, a need so urgent that it requires the full machinery of a bureaucratic age to suppress it, the need to *experience* all manner of different things and draw them into oneself. This is the time, in child-hood and adolescence, when one's intellectual and emotional receptivity is established. The longer this process can con-tinue, and the more variegated the patterns of real interest that are established, the more successful will be the 'develop-ment of the ego' and the subsequent 'individuation-process' (to employ Jungian terminology) that comes with maturity. How can we expect a man to achieve a liberal, balanced out-look if, as a scientist who has specialised in science since the age of fourteen, he has no mental 'schemata' into which he can fit ideas concerning artistic appreciation? Or if, as an arts man, he knows of science only by hearsay as something that went on at school in the 'stinks-lab'?

The suggestions I have to make towards a solution of the problem of Snow's two cultures are, firstly, that we should increase the number and range of required subjects (with options within groups) for entrance to university; secondly, that more subjects be read in the sixth form, and again from different groups; thirdly, that the universities maintain their reputation for teaching in all subjects up to the highest levels possible, even though the level at which the initial lectures of a course are given might have to be lowered. Specialist, voca-tional study can then be regarded as the norm for under-graduates; vocational education not as something opposed to liberal education but as a further extension of it. Subjects have to be dropped at some stage. I believe that at the moment the stage chosen is too early in life, before an overall 'schema' has been developed in the child's mind sufficiently elaborate to serve him as a sympathetic framework for ideas in a wide range of subjects in later life.

It will be objected that it might be found (though personally I doubt it) that under these suggested policies more time would be required if the same standards are to be maintained in the final university examinations in some subjects. Even if the only solution were to increase some or all university courses to four years instead of three, the objections could be only administrative and economic, and these are never insuperable objections. The results would repay the effort handsomely. And we would no longer have such guilty consciences about those 'deprived children' who constitute the members of Snow's two cultures, mutually incomprehensible, mutually incapable of communication.

The Dublin Review, 1960, vol. 484, pp. 126-32.

2

SCIENCE AND
THE PHILOSOPHY OF NATURE

A paper read to the Cambridge University Aquinas Society, 1955

The gulf which exists between the natural sciences and the humanities has become a matter of the deepest concern not merely within the universities but, in view of the frightening powers developed by scientists in recent years, within the general body politic. Solution of the problems which this situation presents would appear to be essential if our civilisation is not to be completely destroyed. In the sphere of education some universities have made efforts to close the gap by the provision of special courses for scientists of lectures in various arts subjects, for arts men in the sciences. Admirable though these ventures are, one feels that the most they will achieve will be to soften the impact between the two sides and to improve inter-faculty relations. It would seem, however, that the underlying need in this current urge for rapprochement is not simply for a more satisfactory symbiosis between what are sometimes thought of as two essentially alien aspects of human endeavour, but rather for a real synthesis of human knowledge and understanding of things and events. Such a synthesis can only be achieved at a much deeper level than those we have mentioned, and in its development it would seem that the professional historian and the professional philosopher have crucial parts to play. It is with considerable misgiving that I, a biological scientist, embark on the question of the scholastic philosopher's contribution to the problem, and if the result appears pretentious I can only plead the importance of the subject: that other minds be encouraged to discuss the issues is much more important than an exposition of my own necessarily immature ideas.

If any single period in history is to be indicated when the present estrangement between science and philosophy really began, it must surely be with Descartes at the beginning of the century of scientific revolution, and this despite Descartes' own dream of a real unification of knowledge within his philosophical system. We scientists, of course, admire Descartes, one of those great men who helped to make modern science possible. But the two philosophical streams, of materialism and idealism, to which cartesian dualism perhaps inevitably gave rise, do seem to represent, by and large, the two sides of the divorce we are considering, and curiously enough both sides are readily to be found amongst scientists themselves: it is a commonplace that in so far as individual scientists admit to a conscious philosophy at all, those who are not materialists tend to be idealists. To my scientific colleagues in either position the title of this paper—'Science and the Philosophy of Nature'—must appear rather puzzling. The reaction of the materialist might be that in so far as one can speak of a philosophy of nature at all one means simply the present corpus of scientific *knowledge* of nature, and that therefore the distinction implied in the title is devoid of meaning. The idealist scientist, on the other hand, would much prefer to concentrate on his laboratory investigations and leave philosophical considerations on one side, at least until after retirement from active academic life, when a volume or two of 'philosophical reflections' might be considered permissible. Thirdly, any scientist who knew the significance to the Thomist of the phrase 'Philosophy of Nature' would be likely to show astonishment that one should even attempt to examine, except as a historical exercise, the relationship between modern science and what he would probably think of as the primitive science of Aristotle's Physics.

It is important to realise that there is much to be said in favour of each of these views. With regard to the attitude of the materialist, it must be remembered that the experimental scientist uses a method which is of its very nature mechanistic: he seeks explanations, by measurement and correlation in terms of material and efficient causes, and endeavours to arrive at a formulation of those general laws which will permit predictions to be made concerning natural phenomena. Now it is characteristic of human nature that that with which one is most deeply and for the longest periods engaged comes to assume for one a position of paramount importance. The surprising thing is not that so many scientists are materialists, but that not all are: for although there is an intrinsic intellectual appeal in scientific pursuits they are bound of course to be ultimately concerned with what is known to some as 'base matter'. Quite apart from specific neo-platonic influences it is perhaps the emotion associated with the word 'base' that lies behind that attitude of disparagement customarily adopted by the arts man towards the scientist. Though why it should be considered better to study the works and follies of man rather than the works of God is not, perhaps, altogether self-evident.

Those scientists who adopt an idealist philosophy are almost obliged to keep their science and their philosophy quite distinct from each other; they thus personify, as it were, the very rupture which we wish to heal. And yet again there is much to be said, pragmatically at least, for their attitude, because experimental science *can* succeed only in so far as its approach is rigidly mechanistic, and the individual scientist is successful only in so far as he has the enthusiasm, the courage and the integrity to follow the scientific method with singleness of purpose. He cannot afford to put his examining instruments on one side and spend his time philosophising about the more intangible aspects of his work because there is always so much in the laboratory still waiting to be done. An exception to this last generalisation should perhaps be made in respect of certain fields of nuclear physics where it appears that further advances in purely scientific knowledge (i.e. of efficient causes) are inherently impossible. The nuclear physicist is in certain respects, it seems, face to face with philosophical problems. He may long to make more accurate and more ingenious measurements, but he finds there is no conceivable way of measuring or correlating his material. At this stage, then, it is not more knowledge of, but rather a deeper understanding of, the nature of things which is required, and the scientist has a positive need of the philosopher. But in all other branches of science work of a strictly scientific nature can proceed almost indefinitely, it would seem, and under these circumstances the scientist does well not to allow a habit of philosophical reflection to dull the edge of his hard-won techniques of objective analysis.

The third likely reaction to the title of this paper of which we spoke, namely, that it implies a necessarily unproductive attempt to harmonise primitive scientific knowledge with that of the present day, has this much to be said in its defence, that one looks in vain in modern expositions of the scholastic 'Philosophy of Nature' for any clear account of its position vis-à-vis modern science. It is perhaps not surprising that Aristotle and Aquinas should not have made the necessary distinction, since one of the terms had not in their ages achieved any degree of individuality. But likewise many modern exponents of the system have failed, out of filial piety, even to recognise that a problem exists, and consequently this part of their exposition is invariably the least satisfactory. The volume entitled *Philosophy of Nature* in a modern Thomist text-book is often a curious mixture of ancient and modern, with ac-

counts of popular science tailored to fit the system and sometimes (but this very rarely) vice versa. Such expositions make
for unhappy reading for the scientist at least, whatever may be
their appeal to the seminarian-philosopher.

And yet the modern scientist, for all his philosophical confusion over cartesian dualism and its subsequent history (and
he has in this matter been largely in the grip of historical
circumstance, due in part to the very success of his own
scientific techniques), the scientist is at heart, one might almost
say by instinct, a philosophical realist—I mean in the modern
sense of the word, the opposite of idealist. If the present gulf
between philosophy and science is to be bridged it can surely
only be done through the medium of a realist philosophy.
One feels, particularly in the present climate of opinion, that a
tremendous opportunity awaits the Thomist philosopher provided that he is prepared, firstly, to make the necessary distinction between the terms of this evening's subject, and
secondly, to use the modern knowledge now at his disposal to
revise or recast where necessary the philosophical distinctions
made by St Thomas on the basis of his vastly inferior scientific
knowledge of the universe. Palaeontology is a fascinating
science, but fossilised philosophy has little to recommend it.
Perhaps this is the real significance of the modern Thomistic
revival. Perhaps our twentieth-century scholastics are destined
not only to atone for the shortcomings of some of their forebears, but even to supply the very keystone of the arch which
so many of today's thinkers are anxious to see built between
the sciences and the humanities.

It has, of course, always been clear to the majority of philosophers, what now the nuclear physicist is perhaps forced to
accept for scientific reasons, that the techniques of science, of
measurement and correlation, are inherently incapable of
giving a complete account of natural phenomena. No matter
how refined or how exhaustive might be the quantitative

techniques of science, they can never abolish the qualitative, because before ever a measurement can be made there must be *something* there to be measured. The scientist accepts implicitly the reality of this raw material of his studies, and it is this instinctive realism which gives him at once a degree of sympathy for and an understanding of the Thomist position: each builds his concept of the nature of reality from the same sense-data. We may recall St Thomas in *de Trinitate* vi. 2. where he says, 'The beginning or principle of every scientific enquiry lies in the senses, and all our intellectual apprehension is abstracted from their data.' It is true that the modern scientist uses more than his unaided senses, but all his techniques are simply refinements or extensions of the senses, and we may be sure that St Thomas would have welcomed all of them in so far as they provide more accurate information about the basic data to which his system of philosophy makes constant appeal. The first, and most fundamental distinction then, between Science and the Philosophy of Nature rests in the fact of *existence*: this is something which the scientist simply accepts—must accept—before he can start to employ his mathematical techniques, but the implications inherent in the fact of existence lie within the province of the Philosophy of Nature, and are complementary, in a most elegant fashion, to the scientist's observations. This quality of complementarity is in fact the distinguishing mark throughout, of these two fields of enquiry into the mode of working of the universe and its significance. However St Thomas himself, as we have said, made no such distinction within his First Order of Abstraction (i.e. Physics). This lack of definition and distinction is what seems to have given rise to so much apparent confusion amongst his successors. If we define Physics (in the Aristotelian sense) as the study of *ens mobile seu sensibile* then we see at once (following Maritain) that the definition falls readily into two complementary parts, the one, *ens*, being that which is *intelligible* (to the philosopher), the other, *mobile seu sensibile*, being that which is *observable* (by the scientist). These constitute, then, the respective fields of Philosophy of Nature and Science of Nature, but having made the distinction let us hasten to emphasise that since both are abstracted from what is a unity neither can be independent of the other; each is complementary to the other, obverse and reverse of a coin which is the reality itself, the thing or the complex of things under consideration. If the mutual rapport is so intimate that mutual independence is impossible, so too it should be clear that neither aspect of the reality can be in any sort of dominance over the other. One of the results of the failure of the classical Scholastics to make this distinction, coupled with their deep sense of the significance of the hierarchies of knowledge, was that philosophy inevitably held a position of dominance over whatever scientific methodology existed, a situation which had to be broken before science could start its truly remarkable advance. In a dramatic passage Jacques Maritain says that 'Science could only reap its harvest in the field of experience when it had removed and smashed the marble slabs on Aristotle's tomb.'[1] We know now something of the price that Europe has had to pay for that destruction, but in the *rapprochement* we are now urging we cannot, even if we would, ignore the great harvest that has been reaped in the field of experience, and it is foolish to think that Scholastic philosophy can ever be the same again. There must in the future be no more brow-beating, by either side, but rather a mutual willingness of scientist and philosopher to learn of the truths which each has discovered.

Now the scientist, as we have said earlier, can readily pursue his studies in most branches without ever stopping to consider the philosophical implications of his findings. There may

1. Maritain, J., *Science et Sagesse*, Eng. trans., Glasgow University Press, 1940, p. 27.

be as a result some impoverishment of his own personality, but his findings lose nothing in respect of their scientific validity. The realist philosopher, however, can never afford to remain in ignorance of the findings of the scientist, because it is precisely on the observations of sense-data that he claims ultimately to base his philosophy. In classical philosophy of course the data are the commonsense observations of everyday life, and about such data there is an element of immediacy which creates a powerful suggestion of their universal validity. This impression may indeed be supported by more detailed investigation, but scientists have not infrequently shown that ordinary sense-data are often either inadequate, only relatively true, or frankly fallacious. Scientific observation, for all its apparent remoteness, is nothing more than common-sense observation pursued more actively and more keenly, and with an acute sense of the need for impartiality and objectivity. There is no doubt that such careful observations are preferable to the more careless ones of everyday life as a basis for a realist philosophy of universal application.

This is not to insist that the philosopher of nature must always wait upon the pronouncements of the scientist. As has been seen, the philosophical problem of existence is logically prior to the scientist's investigations, and philosophical analysis of the fact of Change involves, quite apart from the scientific study of particular changes that occur, a whole range of specifically philosophical concepts expressed by the Thomist as matter and form, quantity and substance, substantial change and accidental change—concepts all of which would be full of meaning for the modern scientist, and would probably prove acceptable to him provided only that the philosopher were capable of applying them to specific examples which the scientist might raise from his own specialised knowledge of the universe.

There are other aspects, though, of the traditional Philosophy of Nature, in which the philosopher can claim no such logical priority. Philosophical analysis of the nature of life (vegetative, sensitive and rational, to speak in scholastic terms) must rest primarily on observation of living organisms themselves. The traditional distinction of the realms of organic life was made on the basis of common everyday experience, and the usefulness of the distinction is recognised today by our division of biology into the two sciences of botany and zoology. But the modern biologist has far greater experience than St Thomas had of the range and distribution of living organisms, and far greater insight into the nature of vital processes. If Thomism is to survive its exponents can no longer afford to limit their thinking about the organic world to that degree of biological knowledge achieved by the ancients. The absolute distinction made by the Schoolmen between vegetative and sensitive life is seen by the modern scholar not to be applicable to some types of 'intermediate' organisms. It would even seem rash today, in view of our increasing knowledge of protein-structure, to build philosophical edifices on an insistence on a fundamental qualitative difference between the worlds of living and non-living matter. We need to investigate the philosophical implications of the concept of, for instance, 'levels of material organisation' as a basis for distinguishing between living and non-living matter.

St Thomas's doctrine of the Unity of Substantial Form, widely debated by his contemporaries, seems to the biologist of today to be largely irrelevant, because we know now how readily living tissues and individual cells can be maintained in states of apparently perfect function quite independently of the organism of which they once formed a part. Similarly we know today how easily, in some species, a single embryo can be induced, either by experiment or in the course of natural events, to become two complete and independent creatures, or, alternatively, to duplicate some but not all of its organs and tissues. Similarly it is practicable, too, to induce two separate, independently-fertilised, ova to join together so intimately that only one individual results from the fusion where once there were two. Theories as to the nature of Substantial Form must consider the curious events which occur in the phenomenon of metamorphosis, and the existence of certain symbiotic relationships in which host and parasite are so inter-dependent that they form in fact one single metabolic system. A revision in this field of scholastic teaching would be most desirable.

Lastly, for the purpose of this paper, there is one general aspect of the Aristotelian system as expounded by many Thomist philosophers and others, which appears to have led to a great deal of general confusion with regard both to the function of the scientist and to the significance of his findings. I refer to the well-known concept of chains of Secondary Causes which lead back, link by link it is implied, to the First Cause who is God. It is perhaps not unlikely that Aristotle himself did conceive of this eminently transcendent deity as being very far removed from the scene of current secondary causes. But such a concept would seem to lead inevitably to the deism which has been so prevalent throughout the period of development of modern science, and to the widespread acceptance of the fallacy that the demonstration of scientific laws somehow implies that God is no longer 'necessary'. Such secularisation of the created universe has progressed apace during the last three centuries, and the impression gained by most people of the advance of science is that it has repeatedly ousted God from the scientific gaps into which deist ideas had despairingly pushed him. We know, of course, that such a travesty of the truth was far from the mind of St Thomas, and his many passages on the constant sustaining action of the First Cause show clearly that for him the concept of Secondary Cause inherently contains the concept of the necessary and constant activity of the First Cause. Forthright exposition of the scholastic doctrine of Contingency might be effective, more than any other single factor, in helping the world out of its predicament concerning the powers and the limits of science. This teaching offers complete freedom to the scientific investigator to search for secondary causes by means of the proper scientific techniques: he can then be confident, in the use of his methods, that they can in no way be interpreted, as they have so often been, as assaults upon the idea of the First Cause, the sustainer of all things.

As we said at the beginning of this paper, the gulf which has been allowed to grow between the Sciences and the Humanities is of frightening proportions, and the results might well be disastrous for our European culture. The contribution which Thomism could make towards averting such a catastrophe is so significant, that it is not perhaps too much to say that the exploration of the kind of problems and difficulties of which we have spoken ought to be regarded as the principal task of the modern Thomist philosopher.

1955.

3

FREEDOM AND CAUSALITY IN BIOLOGY

A paper read to the Newman Philosophy of Science Group, 1956

The subject matter of this paper, as the title was given to me, is so wide in scope that I feel at the outset the need to deny any real competence to speak to the title as it stands. So far as the metaphysical side is concerned I am not even clear as to the meaning in this context of the words 'freedom and causality'; they have so many different uses in ordinary speech. As to biology, I wish to disclaim any qualification as a so-called general biologist, prepared to discuss the significance of each and every biological phenomenon from the activities of a virus to those of the human psyche. It is true that the technological organisation to which I belong—the medical profession—does take within its purview these two extremes of biological organisation. But having left the practice of the art of medicine for enquiry into those basic sciences on which the art is ever dependent, my interests have necessarily become canalised and specialised. As an anatomist I conceive my functions to be two, firstly, the discovery of the arrangement and inter-relationships of the structures that comprise the human body, and secondly, the search for an understanding of how we ever *came* to have such an extraordinarily complicated arrangement of organs and tissues: why, for instance, so often some anatomical structure, a nerve or artery it may be, far from taking a straightforward path from point A to point B, should instead take a most devious route in a way designed, it would seem, specially to trap the unwary medical student. In this intriguing realm of scientific enquiry problems will abound for many decades to come—as yet we have, about most of them, only the vaguest ideas as to possible solutions. From the general biologist's point of view it is a very restricted field, this one of human and animal morphogenesis (for one is almost entirely dependent on animal material, of course, for experimental purposes), but in a way it is one which is central to the whole field of biological enquiry, and indeed to human enquiry of all kinds. We are entirely dependent on our physical bodies for our very existence as human beings. Without the existence of our bodies either already in recognisable human form or potentially so as fertilised human ova—which, to the specialist, can mean in fact 'recognisable human form'—there would never *be* any human souls. Indeed for christians it will not be until after the resurrection of the body that human beings will again be properly reconstituted so to speak, to inherit *as men and women* the kingdom of heaven. Human anatomy is then an eminently respectable study even for the metaphysician and theologian, though I am not of course claiming that it will give him any special insight into what our glorified bodies might be like.

Again, if we adhere to the truism of the mediaeval realists that *nihil in intellectu quod non prius in sensu* we are brought up sharply to realise that it might be as well if we knew a little about the constitution of the organs that give us our sense-appreciations, how they came to be what they are, and how reliable they are in recording events of the external and the internal world.

It would be true to say, I think, that the majority of anatomists until well on into the last century, and many even in the earlier part of this, conceived of their subject solely in terms of the first aspect I mentioned, observation, description, and the compilation of data in ever-increasing detail. This sort of activity has been called the natural history phase through which all science must go. One finds it hard, within the profession, to forgive those colleagues of recent date who still took this 'natural history' view of the subject and brought it into disrepute amongst their fellow-scientists as being concerned only with long, complicated, and largely meaningless lists of the names of things. One has more sympathy with those other, pre-nineteenth century, enquirers who also largely failed to ask questions about human anatomy, whether the 'how' of science or the 'why' of philosophy. For was not man, to them, created as we now see him directly out of the dust and slime of the earth, fashioned in the image and likeness of God in the way visualised by Michelangelo in his 'Creation of Adam'? The result, on the day chronicled in the Book of Genesis, of a divine *fiat*? To ask further questions about our physical structure would, to a believer, imply incipient heresy. In this matter, the biologists of the eighteenth and early nineteenth centuries were virtually all believers, not least because they had the tremendous weight of Linnaeus's scientific authority in support of the view that all species of animals and plants *were* species precisely because they had been so created by God, each species consisting of a distinct and fixed biological unit independent of all others. This eighteenth-century scientific dogma must bear much of the responsibility for the unhappy conflicts of later biological theory. But if it had not been for this unquestioned acceptance of the fixity of species we might have had to wait for a long time before getting a system of biological nomenclature anything like so useful as the binomial system of Linnaeus. In the setting of biological 'fixism', however, *commentary* on human anatomy as distinct from its *description* had perforce to limit itself to metaphysical speculation as to *why* God should have made man as he is. We are all of us familiar, for instance, with the sort of thing that was said (and is still in some circles), about man's having two legs instead of four: he was raised, it has been said, on to two legs instead of being condemned to walk 'like the brutes' (note the emotional overtones) on all fours (that is, if one neglects the kangaroo and some others) so that instead of having to look always on the ground as do the beasts (which they mostly don't) he could raise his eyes the more easily to heaven, as befitted his unique station. Pious things are said, too, about the design of human hands as instruments of prayer, of sacrifice and supplication, and moral truths have been drawn from the relative hairlessness of mankind. Indeed all these things, and many others besides, *are* very puzzling, and one would not like to deny the possibility of some element of truth in these rather fanciful ideas. But if we are looking for anatomical excellence as evidence of the uniqueness of man, we might spare a thought for his comparative awkwardness in the water and his utter incompetence in the air—how much more 'fitting' it would be if the lord of creation could be like the swan, almost equally at home in all three media, *and* look graceful into the bargain. Or let us take the hackneyed example of the pineal gland. Descartes' theory about it was that it constituted the seat of the soul, the one link between mind and body; such an imaginary link or bridge is still searched for by some modern anatomists and physiologists if not by philosophers of the Thomist or the modern logical school. Ever since Descartes' theory about the pineal was put to the test and found wanting, search has been made for the possible significance of this gland in the human. The search has revealed little that could be called significant, as yet. But almost certainly this gland did have a very useful function many millions of years ago, and a fascinating history in between if only it were preserved in fossil forms. There still exist some reptiles in which the pineal functions as a perfectly good organ of vision, an eye situated right on the top of the head, permitting the creature to gaze all day long at the heavens if it so desires. This last *reductio ad absurdum* of certain pious speculations about human anatomy was intended to show how, to an anatomist *qua* scientist, such speculation is quite properly ruled out as irrelevant to his study. A Catholic anatomist might, in addition, be tempted to rule out a good deal of this sort of speculation for quite other reasons—an apologetic which speaks of biological organisation in terms of 'design' and 'plan' is, firstly, at a hopeless disadvantage when it comes to the sort of biological *dis*organisation with which the anatomist and embryologist is only too familiar; secondly, such an apologetic carries with it unmistakable overtones of philosophical deism, officially condemned, I believe, as heretical; and thirdly, there is in the view of creation which this outlook implies and may even overtly expound, an idea of a magical, wonder-working God which is a complete travesty of the christian concept of the omnipresent sustainer of all things. If only nineteenth-century christians had been aware of the dangers inherent in such naive views, how different might have been the history of the relations between religion and biological theory. If only the average Catholic of today were aware of them, how different might be the correspondence-columns of some of the English Catholic newspapers!

The study of anatomy underwent its most profound revolution after Darwin. Acceptance of a general theory of evolution (as distinct from the various theories which were expounded as to *how* biological evolution occurred) acted as a tremendous stimulus to anatomical enquiry. Such enquiry was bound still to be largely of the natural history variety, but at least now it became seemingly respectable scientifically, in that the observations could always be interpreted in terms of evolutionary theory. In the enthusiasm of the period some of the interpretations were manifestly absurd, resting as they did on wild speculation of a hopelessly unverifiable kind. For an excellent criticism of such pseudo-science reference might be made to certain paragraphs in W. R. Thompson's introduction to the new Everyman edition of *The Origin of Species*—an essay, one might add, to be regarded not with unmixed approval.

But despite local excesses the more accurate concept did firmly establish itself that animal species and, *a fortiori*, their organs and tissues, were not necessarily immutable, not any more than we now believe the chemical elements to be, though it is not long since such a notion would have been condemned as the nonsense-talk of mediaeval alchemy. Once the inherent plasticity of biological organisation had been recognised, the way was open for investigation into the causal factors involved in such changes as were recognised to occur. Also, since knowledge of the normal is a necessary preliminary in biology to investigation of the experimentally-induced abnormality, it became necessary to know in increasing detail the factors responsible for normal ontogenetic development. It was at this stage that the Natural Selection theory of Darwin's followers became in a real way an anti-scientific force, because Darwinians only concerned themselves with the selection or rejection by nature of established changes in anatomical structure. The fascinating study of how those changes had come about was dismissed as irrelevant, the result of an inexplicable chance. Today, of course, the two sciences of experimental embryology and genetics have a wealth of achievement behind them, and since about 1930 their findings have been increasingly incorporated into a neo-Darwinian synthesis of evolutionary theory which goes a long way towards 'saving the phenomena', which is all that one asks of any scientific theory.

Biological enquiry, in so far as my own field of morphogenesis is concerned, is essentially analytical and strictly mechanistic. Whether scope can be found in certain fields of biological theory for each of Aristotle's four types of 'cause', the anatomist as such only ever has to postulate material and efficient causes. To illustrate the point, and at the same time

to try to give you some insight into the outlook of the anatomist, I will outline to you a small enquiry in which I was recently
engaged.

A colleague from the Department of Pathology had done a
post-mortem on a new-born infant who had a combination of
three congenital abnormalities, namely absence of the spleen,
malformation of the heart and a partial inversion of the internal organs, that is, something like a mirror-image of the
normal. This particular 'triad', as such combinations of three
anomalies are called, has been well-known to pathologists for
over a hundred years, and many examples have been described
in the medical literature.

The factors concerned in the production of congenital
abnormalities in general can be classed under two headings,
firstly genetic, i.e. occurring as the result of a mutation or an
unfavourable recombination of genes in the germ-plasm, and
secondly environmental, that is when unfavourable factors
operate on a normal healthy embryo so as to prevent its
proper development. In any given case one attempts an interpretation on either the one or the other of these alternatives,
on the general scientific principle that hypotheses are not to be
unnecessarily multiplied. Indeed protagonists of each view
have been known irrationally to try to force *all* cases into
one only of the two categories. There is abundant experimental evidence that in animal populations both factors can
result in apparently identical abnormalities in the phenotype.
If the effect is due to genetic factors it will of course be incorporated also into the genotype. There is abundant evidence
too that so far as man is concerned, in this respect as in all
others affecting the *soma*, we are not immune from the sort of
adverse conditions which affect the rest of the animal kingdom.

The aetiology of the particular triad which my colleague
had come across is as yet unknown, but it has always been

considered that in view of some fairly constant anomalies in the large arteries leading from the heart the time of onset of the condition must be during the sixth and seventh weeks of intrauterine life, the period in which the main arteries become established as distinct entities. Since there had not been reported any history of maternal illness or indisposition during this period, or anything to suggest an exogenous aggression on the embryo, it had been concluded, despite the absence of any compelling genetic evidence, that the condition as a whole must be genetically determined, the result of 'a mutation with pleiotropic effects', as the jargon puts it.

Now briefly, what we were able to do from examination of the case which came under our notice was to date the onset of the abnormalities, with quite fair precision, between the twenty-third and the twenty-seventh days after the mother's ovulation. This dating was possible from a detailed study of the pattern of the *veins* which drain into the heart, and was confirmed on examination of the heart from a previous case which had been preserved in the Department of Pathology. This finding allows us now to advance the hypothesis that environmental factors might well be the cause of the condition. It may well be that the small uterine haemorrhages which the mother-to-be not uncommonly experiences about this time or shortly before it, might in a few instances produce a temporary interference with the nutrition of the developing organism, and set in train a series of events leading eventually to the fully-established abnormalities.

Such a hypothesis agrees well with experimental studies of embryo-genesis in lower organisms. In human studies experimental techniques are out of the question in this sort of problem, and time alone and the collection of a large enough series of carefully-recorded cases will serve to substantiate or invalidate the new hypothesis. But the point of the story is to emphasise that in this enquiry, and in countless others like it, the biologist rightly confines his attention to consideration of material and efficient causes of the phenomena he is considering. It might be objected that in this case we were dealing with the abnormal, and that such studies form an insecure basis for the development of biological theory. The objection will be answered in two ways. Firstly, the layman might be forgiven for thinking that in this sort of case we are dealing with comparatively rare biological phenomena. In this supposition he would perhaps be joined by many 'general biologists' for they, like the force of Natural Selection, tend to use the biological successes and ignore the failures. But in medicine the failures cannot be ignored. They are the *raison d'être* of the art. In the question of human congenital abnormalities it is estimated that one in three (certainly one in five) embryos die from natural causes. Such figures make the question of faulty morphogenesis an integral part of the total biological scene, and must be taken account of in one's 'philosophy of biology' in a way not usually attempted by writers on the subject. A second answer to the objection we raised about arguing to the normal from the study of the abnormal, is that all the findings both in genetics and in experimental embryology go to show that in matters of normal morphogenesis, too, causal chains or networks of a strictly mechanistic type are involved at all stages, and await elucidation by the experimental scientist. This sort of enquiry, fundamentally mechanistic in approach, is, in my opinion, the only proper one to adopt in the branches of biological science we have been considering. What sort of a metaphysic the individual scientist professes is, of course, a matter quite distinct from his scientific activities. He can, if he wishes, extend the scope of his mechanistic outlook and construct a materialist philosophy, a thorough-going mechanism or a phenomenalism. But he has no scientific warrant for doing so. On the other hand he may wish to install a few ghosts in his biological machines (biologists are continually doing so) and call himself a vitalist. Again he has no scientific warrant, because again he is now considering questions not of physics but of metaphysics. The practical realism of the Thomist concept that the 'form' or 'soul' of any created thing is simply its 'principle of organisation', dependent on and inseparable from its 'matter', alone seems to allow full scope for both scientific and metaphysical enquiry.

So much for the world of the traditional biologist. Whether he be anatomist, physiologist, biochemist or psychologist, he proceeds in his enquiries by observation and analysis, formulation of hypotheses, deduction of the probable consequences and the testing of them by experiment where practicable or by further observation where experiment is impracticable or impossible. He looks for material and efficient causes of biological phenomena and, finding them, has no need and no business as a scientist to postulate wholly unverifiable factors such as 'freedom' or 'purpose' as entering into the biological picture. When some factor, even if certainly present, is in essence not verifiable, then it cannot be dealt with by the scientific method.

It is obvious that biology on these terms, that is biology as a strict science, can never give more than a partial account of the phenomena of living things. It can only account partially for 'how' and never for 'why'. It is not surprising, then, that throughout the history of modern biological research there have always been individuals, conscious in their researches of the overwhelming beauty of living organisms, and of the evident purposes and directiveness of their activities, who have refused to restrict themselves to explanations in mechanical terms, and have sought a more complete and intellectually satisfying account of vital processes. It is no accident that in recent years, with the swing away from yet further analysis of the *parts* of living creatures, and with the development of the study called 'animal behaviour', i.e. the study of the activities of *whole* creatures both in isolation and community, there has been an increase in the number of biologists (wholly respectable from the scientific point of view) who have rejected the naive mechanism of the older schools, mechanism with or without ghosts. So for instance, Professor G. P. Wells (the son of the late H. G.) in his inaugural professorial lecture at University College, London dismissed the older philosophy of biology in a single sentence: 'When I was a young man I was a mechanist of the most bone-headed type—believing that behaviour was nothing more than a series of reflexes.' Dr L. E. R. Picken, the Cambridge zoologist, in the *School Science Review* for 1955 says: 'We can never expect to be able to say "Cells divide because . . ." where the final term is some statement such as "because the concentration of a particular metabolite reaches a maximum value". For even if this final term is true, it can never be more than a partial statement of the whole situation. The causal explanation resolves into an autology, "Cells divide because cells divide", and we must recognise and accept that any enquiry directed towards the explanation of cellular processes in simple-minded commonsense causal terms is addressed to an unattainable objective.'

It is interesting that realisations, such as these, of the limitations of the Victorian approach to biology, should be voiced from within the science itself. Voiced indeed at the level of the presidential address to the zoology section of the British Association's meeting in Sheffield. Dr W. H. Thorpe is one of this country's leaders in the field of animal behaviour. While much of his work has gone to show, in a very elegant fashion, how many fantastically complicated behaviour patterns of animals and birds are determined and controlled by genetic and environmental factors, in much the same way as are morphological patterns, yet some aspects of behaviour apparently will not fit into the mechanist's mould, and Thorpe has been led to postulate an element of true 'conscious-purpose' in sub-human organisms. We have thus arrived at an intriguing situation, where many human psychologists (the 'behaviourists' being the dominant group) deny to the human psyche what a leading zoologist regards as essential to the psyche of sub-human species. Dr Thorpe was reported by *The Times* as having made a plea at the British Association's meeting for 'a carefully thought out combination of objective and subjective approach' as the appropriate scientific tool for elucidating some of the more intricate manifestations of biological organisation. Here again one can only sympathise with the need that is felt for a more comprehensive view than has been given by traditional biology. But it is terribly important, I think, that we should realise fully that what is being advocated is a combination of physics and metaphysics, and that if we adopt the suggestion then we should be clear in our minds, at all stages of the enquiry, as to which approach is being used, and clear too as to the powers and limits of each separate discipline. If a natural scientist is to have freedom to introduce, under the name of science, metaphysical concepts into scientific theory and experiment, and to do so without perhaps realising what he is doing, one can envisage the complete collapse of scientific discipline and progress.

To sum up: I have tried to limit the scope of this paper largely to the field of biology with which I am most familiar. In this field I have argued that material and efficient causes are all that should be postulated from the scientific point of view as 'explanations' of biological phenomena. Final and formal causality are, I think, metaphysical concepts which have no place in the strictly scientific approach to biological phenomena, for all that they are indispensable for a more complete understanding. The inadequacy of the traditional scientific approach, as seeing no more than one facet of the totality of truth, is recognised by many modern biologists, but the solution to the intellectual dilemma would appear to be not the adulteration of scientific methods by those of metaphysics, whether wittingly or not, but rather by the recognition of the need for both methods and for the maintenance of the integrity of each by rigorous self-discipline.

1956.

4

THE IMPACT OF DARWIN'S 'ORIGIN OF SPECIES' ON MEDICINE AND BIOLOGY

A paper read to the Sixth British Congress 1967 on the History of Medicine: 'Medicine and Science in the 1860's'

The last ten years have seen published a greater volume of 'Darwiniana' than any decade in history, and there is as yet no sign of abatement.[1] The recent impetus came, of course, from the centennial celebrations in 1958 of the publication of the Darwin-Wallace papers and, in 1959, that of Darwin's greatest single book, *On the Origin of Species by Means of Natural Selection; or the preservation of favoured races in the struggle for life*. I give it its full title, because it represents an exact summary of Darwin's particular creative insight into one very important aspect of the evolutionary process. The origin and evolution of species had been much discussed during the previous hundred years, but never before in these specific terms. It was this personal creative act, a 'bisociation' typical of advances in knowledge,[2] that led Darwin initially to speak of 'my' theory. This expression he subsequently modified or dropped, when he realised (a) that none of his ideas were in fact

1. Fleming, Donald, in 'The Centenary of *The Origin of Species*' (Review Article), *J. Hist. Ideas*, 1959, **20**, 437-46, lists many of the books published about that time. Other books, and articles in specialist journals, have appeared at regular intervals since then. Professional historians are displacing the amateurs. Any volume of the *Journal of the History of Ideas* is liable to carry two or three full-length articles on Darwinism, and the subject is included in a Special Period Course for Part II of the Cambridge Historical Tripos 1968.
2. Koestler, Arthur, *The Act of Creation*, Hutchinson, London, 1964.

unique to him, and (b) that, as he had known all along, his own theory of evolution involved a great deal more than 'natural selection, or the preservation of favoured races in the struggle for life'.

Another reason for giving in full, and for emphasising, the title of a book usually referred to as the *Origin of Species* or simply as the *Origin*—the single-word title being a mark of extreme distinction—is that, in the result, it was precisely the *narrow* view (as I call it, though Professor C. D. Darlington would doubtless call it the *hard* view[3]) of evolution that, in the hands of Darwinists and neo-Darwinists, received most of the publicity and hence captured the market. This is the view that the process of evolution results solely from the natural selection of biological variations that came to be thought of (though not by Darwin) as wholly random in nature and fortuitous in onset. This doctrine added one of its strongest planks to the platform of 'traditional' British empiricism. By Sir Arthur Keith it was elevated still further: his 1925 Conway lecture[4] was entitled *The Religion of a Darwinist*, a religion where the two dominant forces were chance and struggle. Darwin might have been disappointed had he known in the 1860's that this one part of his extraordinarily complex theory, of which the *Origin* represented only what he called an 'abstract of an abstract', would become so powerful that to question its all-embracing efficacy (as did W. R. Thompson in his introduction to the current Everyman edition of the *Origin*,[5] or as Sir Alister Hardy recently did in his Gifford lectures[6]) would be to court that curiously emotional con-

3. Darlington, C. D., *Darwin's Place in History*, Blackwell, Oxford, 1959.
4. Keith, Sir Arthur, *The Religion of a Darwinist*, Rationalist Series, Watts & Co., London, 1925.
5. Thompson, W. R., Introduction to *The Origin of Species*, Everyman Edition, Dent, London, 1956.
6. Hardy, Sir Alister, *The Living Stream: Evolution and Man*, Collins, London, 1966.

tempt reserved by some modern biologists for anyone who hesitates about adopting a neo-Darwinian philosophy which in fact leads logically to the emptiness and meaninglessness of certain forms of modern existentialism, and finally to the abandoning of science as a really significant human activity. Darwin himself must of course take some responsibility for the restrictions from which his thought has suffered: if an author incorporates an important and true hypothesis into both the title and the subtitle of his book, he cannot really complain if disciples choose to emphasise this one more than others (of which in fact there are a great many in the *Origin*). My thesis is that what emerged out of the conflict in the 1860's, namely the philosophy of Darwinism, was a *hairesis*, a choosing, for non-scientific reasons, of one part of a complex whole. In other words, what we know as Darwinism is, so far as Darwin and the *Origin* are concerned, a 'heresy' in the literal meaning of that much-abused word.

It is clear that the *Origin* created what T. S. Kuhn[7] calls a paradigmatic situation. A paradigm is a framework of ideas, a system which, amongst other functions, determines what will and what will not be admissible in future as scientific evidence. There is currently some debate amongst philosophers of science as to the precise status of paradigms.[8] Whether they turn out to be primarily sociological forces, or metaphysical insights, or theological attitudes, one thing seems fairly certain: they are not 'scientific statements' in the inductive sense of Bacon. They are, then, at any rate, 'philosophical' in the broad sense. Darwin elaborated a very complicated paradigm. Biological scientists and medical scientists appear to have handled it in ways that illustrate both advantages and drawbacks to what one might call the 'relatively

7. Kuhn, T. S., *The Structure of Scientific Revolutions*, University of Chicago Press, 1962
8. Masterman, Margaret, in *Theoria to Theory*, 1967, I, 345-50.

harder' and the 'relatively softer' sciences. It is possible to be hard and rigorous only about what is relatively simple. The more complex the situation, in other words the greater the number of variables involved, the larger will be the inevitable percentage-error, and the softer the result of what can only be an imperfect analysis. Nothing is to be gained from making value-judgements about such different experimental situations. Now it is clear that medicine is a 'softer' science than most. If medical scientists had been more involved in the public debate on Darwinism in the 1860's, the paradigm might not have suffered the reductions it did. Though there were more significant journals extant than the *Lancet*[9] it is of interest that the first reference to Darwin in that journal appears to have been as late as 1866[10]: the reviewer of the new edition of Todd and Bowman's *Physiological Anatomy and Physiology of Man*[11] noted that 'a slight sketch of Darwin's theory of the origins of species is introduced, with some very sound strictures upon its general applicability.' What looks possibly like medical isolation from the general stream of science did not result from want

9. Ellegård, in the preface to his comprehensive study (Ellegård, Alvar, 'Darwin and the general reader: the reception of Darwin's theory of Evolution in the British Periodical Press 1859-1872', *Acta Univ. Gothoburg*, 1958, **64**, 1-394), in referring to 'general' as compared with 'purely scientific' journals, says, 'In the latter, scientists concentrated on details; in the former, where they addressed a wider public, they treated the problems from a more general point of view.' He adds a footnote, of interest to the historian of medicine: 'It is significant that such a purely scientific journal as the *London, Edinburgh and Dublin Philosophical Magazine* contained no single article during the whole of the period 1859-1872 where the Darwinian theory was discussed. On the other hand, the *British and Foreign Medico-Chirurgical* (*sic*) reviewed fully the *Origin of Species*, as well as the *Descent of Man* and other books of Darwinian import.' Ellegård possibly didn't realise that the reviewer was Carpenter (a very competent scientist) who was also editor of the journal, nor that he had been, as some might put it, 'nobbled' by Darwin even before the publication of the *Origin* (*v. infra*).

10. Anon, *Lancet*, 1866 (2), p. 185.

11. Todd, R. B., Bowman, W., and Beale, L. S., *The Physiological Anatomy and Physiology of Man*, Part I, Longmans, London, 1866.

of trying. In 1863 a *Lancet* leader[12] had said, with reference to the main forum of scientific debate at the time, 'The British Association for the Advancement of Science avoids two things —Medicine and Morals. It is so intensively and exclusively fond of the physical and the demonstrable, of what can be measured, or seen, or weighed, or put into a crucible, or converted into a fossil, that anything minus these qualities has but a poor chance of being noticed by it. Accordingly it gives the go-by to Medicine and Morals. We think this a matter for regret on two grounds. Firstly, that the subjects ignored by the British Association suffer from its neglect; and secondly that the British Association suffers by neglecting them.' Of course, then as now medicine was constantly under attack for being unscientific. Huxley, in his address in 1866 at St Mary's Hospital,[13] told the tale of the fight between Nature and Disease, with a blindfolded doctor hitting out with a stick, sometimes catching the one and sometimes the other. But he added a neat twist by saying that of course the doctor really was quite acute and therefore, being unable to see very much, he would normally, as a prudent man, abstain from doing anything.

I want now to refer to some of the medical men of the period who did react to Darwin, and who reacted on him. They were important, to my mind, in preventing Darwin from becoming a Darwinist. They constantly reminded him that the simple formula of 'chance followed by blind necessity' was unlikely to prove adequate to handle all the phenomena that the doctor sees in practice. I limit my remarks to medical scientists not only because of the nature of this conference, but also because recent publications have covered fairly well the reactions of non-medical scientists and others, whereas there

12. Anon, *Lancet*, 1863 (2), p. 368.
13. Huxley, Thomas Henry, 'The Relationship of Physical Science to Medical Science and Education', reported in the *Lancet*, 1866 (1), p. 521.

is a curious dearth of recent comment on medical men like Bastian, Carpenter, Humphry, Virchow, Maudsley, Gairdner, Lawson Tait and Paget, all of whom were certainly involved in the private debate, and sometimes in its public manifestations. Furthermore, there was Blackley, whose classic work on hay-fever[14] owed much to Darwin. And Ross's long-forgotten book *The Graft Theory of Disease*[15] contains, amongst much nonsense, an excellent account of the development of vaccination-reactions, both local and systemic, and includes an attempt to explain the latter on the basis of Darwin's 'gemmules', those microscopic carriers of biological information, as we would now say, which were an integral part of his evolutionary theory. There is much to be said (and I hope to say it some day) about this neglected part of Darwin's theory. For the moment it might just be noted that this idea, for confirmation of which he searched his presentation copy of Virchow's book in 1860,[16] is something like the modern biochemical interpretation of immunity and of the auto-immune diseases. For the time, gemmules were masked, or overwhelmed, by germs, more popular by far as the cause of disease and of its spread. In the matter of survival of scientific ideas a period of hibernation is rarely fatal. A temporarily eclipsed hypothesis may find itself eventually rediscovered in

14. Blackley, Charles H., *Experimental Researches on the Causes and Nature of Catarrhus Aestivus (Hay-fever or Hay-asthma)*, Bailliere, Tindall & Cox, London, 1873. The copy in the Darwin Library in Cambridge is inscribed 'To Chas. Darwin Esq., M.A., F.R.S. etc. etc. with the author's compliments.' It was closely read and annotated by the recipient.

15. Ross, James, *The Graft Theory of Disease, being an Application of Mr Darwin's Hypothesis of Pangenesis to the Explanation of the Phenomena of the Zymotic Diseases*, Churchill, London, 1872. The Darwin Library copy is inscribed 'from the author'.

16. Virchow, Rudolph, *Cellular Pathology as based upon Physiological and Pathological Histology*, 2nd edition translated by F. Chance, Churchill, London, 1860. The Darwin Library copy is inscribed 'Charles Darwin, Esq., F.R.S. with the compliments of the Author and of the Translator'.

a safe ecological niche, or even, as with those of Mendel, elevated to the heights. Darwin's gemmules have many counterparts in current biological theory. He had used the concept privately since about 1840[17] in his search for the explanation of biological variation. He always preferred, like any self-respecting scientist who does not prejudge and preclude analysis because of personal philosophical predilections, to look for the causes of things and their ordering, rather than throw in the sponge, as so many have done on the question of variation, and ascribe it merely to chance.

Darwin had many close connections with medical men. There is no indication that his regard for his father's profession was, in general, ever less than profound. He had studied in detail Lawrence's famous 1819 lectures on Man,[18] where noble blows were struck for scientific freedom against the metaphysicians and theologians. Lawrence also said, (wisely it might now be thought), with regard to the speculation that 'man and monkey, or at least the orang-utan, belong to the same species' (as propounded by Monboddo and Rousseau) that it was a notion 'as false, philosophically, as the moral and political consequences, to which it would lead, are shocking and detestable.' One thinks of Huxley's irresponsible boast about his working-class audiences two generations later: 'By next Friday evening they will all be convinced that they are monkeys.'[19] Darwin must not, of course, be held to account

17. Darwin, Francis, ed., *The Life and Letters of Charles Darwin* (hereafter LLD), 3 vols, Murray, London, 1887. Vol. iii, p. 72, letter of 22 August 1867 to Lyell.

18. Lawrence, William, *Lectures on Physiology, Zoology and the Natural History of Man*, 1st edition, London, 1819, subsequently reprinted many times although the author was forced to withdraw his sanction (see Darlington, *op. cit.*).

19. Huxley, Leonard, ed., *Life and Letters of Thomas Henry Huxley*, 3 vols, Macmillan, London, 1908. Vol. 1, p. 276, letter of 22 March 1861 to his wife.

for all or even many of his 'general agent's' sparkling witticisms, the frequent asperity of which caused the *Lancet* to say in 1862, that 'the fling and the sneer, however smart, will only recoil upon himself.'[20] But Darwin was not averse to applauding fisticuffs from afar, as when he wrote to congratulate Huxley on his 1879 preface to Haeckel's new book: 'It is capital, and I enjoyed the tremendous rap on the knuckles which you gave Virchow at the close. What a pleasure it must be to write as you can do.'[21] Debunking is an old method of satisfying aggressive instincts, and Huxley was a past master at it.

The distinguished physician Sir Henry Holland was a friend of Darwin's. Somewhat to the latter's surprise, he became a supporter (with reservations) of the evolutionary hypothesis. When Darwin was soliciting reviews of the *Origin* prior to publication he wrote to W. B. Carpenter, an important physiologist who did much to popularise the general theory of evolution within the medical profession. Darwin warned him, 'You will have a tough job even to shake in the slightest degree Sir H. Holland.'[22] But in 1868 he could write to Hooker, concerning his 'beloved child' pangenesis, which he feared might be still-born, 'Old Sir H. Holland says he has read it twice, and thinks it very tough; but believes that sooner or later "some view akin to it" will be accepted.'[23] This judgement coincided with Darwin's own, not only in 1868 but throughout the subsequent long years of neglect of pangenesis. Perhaps it is only now, a century later, that it will be vindicated by the molecular biologists.

Towards the end of the decade Darwin read and annotated

20. Anon, *Lancet*, 1862 (2), p. 487.
21. Darwin, Francis and Seward, A. P., ed., *More Letters of Charles Darwin* (hereafter MLD), 2 vols, Murray, London. Vol. 1, p. 383, letter no. 294, 19 April 1879 to T. H. Huxley.
22. LLD, Vol. ii, p. 222, letter of 18 November 1859 to W. B. Carpenter.
23. LLD, Vol. iii, p. 78, letter of 23 February 1868 to Hooker.

the books of Maudsley,[24] the neurologist. This fact, together
with the presence of other annotated medical works in the
Darwin Library at Cambridge, shows how closely he followed
the development of scientific medicine. In keeping with his
distaste, by then, for philosophy, is his neglect of the section
in Maudsley's 1870 book entitled *The Limits of Philosophical
Enquiry*. This was a well-argued protest at the manipulation of
science to serve the ends of the positivist philosophy of
Comte, a protest to which Huxley also contributed[25] because
of the charges of positivism which were threatening the
Darwinian camp. It is a pity that Darwin failed to read
Maudsley on the dangers of 'identifying the character of an
epoch of thought with the doctrines of some eminent man who
has lived and laboured and taken the lead in it.' Not that
Darwin could have stopped the process where he himself was
concerned: long before the end of the decade the matter was
well out of his hands and into those of his followers.

One of the first scientists to give an appreciative but critical
comment in public on the *Origin* was the medical botanist
Daubeny of Oxford. It is well known that a meeting was held
in Daubeny's rooms after the notorious Huxley-Wilberforce
clash at the British Association meeting in 1860. Because of
this it has sometimes been assumed (e.g. by Himmelfarb[26])
that Daubeny was one of the early band of disciples. But his
own paper[27] at that meeting was a careful criticism on purely

24. Maudsley, Henry, (1) *The Physiology and Pathology of Mind*, Macmillan,
London, 1867. (2) *Body and Mind: an Enquiry into their Connection and Mutual
Influence, specially in Reference to Mental Disorders*, with appendix, Macmillan,
London, 1870.
25. Huxley, Thomas Henry, 'The Scientific Aspects of Positivism', *The
Fortnightly Review*, 1869, reprinted in *Lay Sermons, Addresses and Reviews*,
Macmillan, London, 1870.
26. Himmelfarb, Gertrude, in *Darwin and the Darwinian Revolution*, Chatto
and Windus, London, 1959.
27. Daubeny, Charles, 'Remarks on the final causes of the sexuality of plants,

scientific grounds, with insistence that theologians should keep out of the discussion. He was concerned about Darwin's problems over the origin of variation and the mechanism of its inheritance. This paper shows that Sir Gavin de Beer, in his recent book on Darwin,[28] is plainly wrong in saying that Darwin anticipated classical genetics. De Beer says, 'Without the benefit of this modern knowledge, Darwin had put his finger on the importance of variation and the fact that it results from sexual reproduction.' But in fact it was Daubeny who countered Darwin by saying about plants that 'whilst in seeds variation is the rule, in buds it is the exception.' Darwin was not put off, and after his book on Variation was published he reiterated in a letter in 1868, 'By the way, let me add that I discussed bud-variation chiefly from a belief which is common to several persons, that all variability is related to sexual generation; I wished to show clearly that this was an error.'[29] If the occupational disease of historians is a kind of diplopia, that leads one to look to the future when one thinks one is looking to the past, it may be that the disorder is more severe for one who has been concerned, like de Beer, with actually influencing future attitudes. Of course, this author takes us only to what has been called the classical or first stage of genetics.

---

with particular reference to Mr Darwin's work on the origin of species. Being the substance of a paper read before the Natural History Section of the British Association for the Advancement of Science, at the meeting held at Oxford in 1860', Parker, Oxford, 1860. Reprinted in *Miscellanies*, a two-volumed collection of Daubeny's essays published by Parker, 1867. This collection (vol. 1) includes a judicious summary, in an 1865 address, of the views for and against Darwinism: on p. 196 he says, 'Still, looking at the Darwinian theory, as alone it ought to be regarded, simply with reference to its scientific merits, there is much to induce us to suspend our judgement until further evidence be afforded.'

28. de Beer, Sir Gavin, *Charles Darwin: Evolution by Natural Selection*, Nelson, London, 1963, p. 86.

29. LLD, Vol. iii, p. 86, letter of 23 June 1868 to G. Bentham.

According to Michie[30] we are already in the third stage. Who will turn out to be right when we enter the fourth stage is anybody's guess. But the story points to the dangers of all rigid orthodoxies in science.

Darwin corresponded with Lawson Tait, the Birmingham gynaecologist who sent him the results of experiments on the adaptive value of the mouse's tail,[31] and with Sir James Paget, whose 1868 letter of thanks for the Variation volume is worth quoting for its comment on medicine in that decade: 'I expect to be made even more than I am now ashamed of my ignorance (and I fear I may add that of my profession too) on the influence of inheritance on the variations and mixtures of diseases. But I hope that my deeper shame may be the beginning of deeper knowledge.'[32]

Three of Paget's former pupils were Professors of Anatomy during this period: Rolleston at Oxford, who supported both Darwin and Huxley publicly (though again with reservations) throughout the decade; Turner at Edinburgh, who corresponded with Darwin and gets a mention in the published letters—though the important ones were unknown until 1919, when Turner's biography was published; and Humphry at Cambridge, about whom, for all his eminence in medicine and science, in medical education and in the '70's campaign (with Darwin and Huxley) about vivisection, there is a curious silence in most of the literature. Humphry is a worthy subject for a medical historian. In this paper I can quote from only one of his publications. His 1866 presidential address[33]

30. Michie, Donald, 'The third stage in genetics,' in *A Century of Darwin*, ed. S. A. Barnett, Heinemann, London, 1958.
31. MLD, Vol. 1, p. 358.
32. Paget, Stephen, ed., *Memoirs and Letters of Sir James Paget*, 3rd edition, Longmans Green, London, p. 414, letter to Darwin dated 29 January 1868.
33. Humphry, G. M., 'Address in Physiology, delivered at the Meeting of the British Association at Nottingham', *J. Anat. Physiol. Lond.*, 1867, **1**, 1-14.

to the section of physiology of the British Association was used to inaugurate, in 1867, the highly-respected *Journal of Anatomy and Physiology* of which he was one of the founder editors. With regard to the physical changes that would be necessary to transform, by evolution, the foot, brain and larynx of ape to man, he says: 'It is possible that such changes might be effected. One would fancy it probable; but we have at present too little right to assume it.' No one today, of course, would be prepared to argue the particular case that he was challenging. Later in the address he says: 'Neither do I think that much direct assistance has been given by the theory of Natural Selection based upon the Struggle for Existence, ably propounded after long and careful research and ably defended as it has been. It has dispersed some of the fallacies and false objections which beset the idea of transmutation of species and has placed the question in a fairer position for discussion; but it reminds us forcibly of some of the real difficulties and objections.'

This was the sort of criticism that Darwin had rightly feared. Huxley's polemical role was essential in shouting it down, and in persuading the public over the heads of scientists. Whether the success of the Darwinism that emerged was really in the interests of science is very debatable. Darwin had originally hoped and expected that his theory would act as a great incentive to research; so it did, but, because of its final emasculated form of 'chance and blind necessity', the research tended to be sterile, because purely descriptive. Picken showed in 1956[34] that the work of the great Wilhelm His was gravely hampered by orthodox Darwinists, who saw nothing to investigate in his science of experimental embryology; and the absurd lengths to which unscientific speculation on mimicry was taken, formed one of the grounds for Thompson's criti-

34. Picken, Laurence, 'The Fate of Wilhelm His', *Nature*, London, 1956, 178, 1162-5.

cisms in the same year.[35] A paradigm which excludes genuine investigation and includes only what is either merely descriptive or phoney is always a danger to the advancement of science.

As a last example, though, of a medical man whose influence assisted Darwin in the 1860's we might take Sir William Gairdner. He was Professor of Medicine in Glasgow alongside Lister. This was also when the erroneous computation, by another Glasgow colleague the future Lord Kelvin, of the physical age of the earth, put the whole Darwinian theory temporarily into jeopardy at the end of the decade. Gairdner's published addresses given to medical students in 1855, 1866 and 1882[36] show his admiration for the natural sciences and for Darwin's work in particular. But, like other medical scientists, he always placed the narrow view of the Darwinists within the larger paradigm that modern research is busy constructing. Gairdner's eulogy of Darwin in his 1888 address[37] as President of the British Medical Association is one of the most profound assessments of the status of this 'man of the century'. When historians eventually reach a conclusion about Darwin's position, it will surely be on one of those very high peaks that are reserved for men of both genius and integrity.

In *Medicine in the 1860's: Proceedings of the Sixth British Congress on the History of Medicine*, 1967. Edited by F. N. L. Poynter. Royal Historical Medical Library, London, 1968.

35. Thompson, W. R., *op. cit.*
36. Gairdner, Sir William Tennant, *Medical Education, Character and Conduct*, Maclehose, Glasgow, 1883.
37. Gairdner, Sir William Tennant, 'The Physician as Naturalist', *British Medical Journal*, 1888 (2), 275-84.

A RADIO BROADCAST:
THE DIFFERENCE TO ME

The University of Cambridge employs me to teach anatomy to medical students. The research work I do may look at times to bear little direct relationship to the subject of anatomy as it is normally understood. But in fact when I study, say, the microscopic structure of chick and rabbit embryos, or when I operate on fetal rats to investigate growth processes long before the animals are born, or when I study the bones of animals now extinct, or when I do the work of trying to think about these things (and thinking is the only single activity which can really justify the existence of academic people like myself) all my work is geared to trying to understand how the human body is constructed and how it has all come about.

Almost everybody, in my experience, has some sort of interest, whether healthy or morbid, in human anatomy. You remember how H. G. Wells describes the effect of an anatomical illustration on young Kipps: '. . . he came upon a striking plate, in which a youth of agreeable profile displayed his interior in an unstinted manner to the startled eye. It was a new view of humanity altogether for Kipps, and it arrested his mind. "Chubes", he whispered, "Chubes".'

A medical student, during the long hours he spends in the dissecting-room, anatomising with scalpel and forceps the human corpses that form the material of his study, easily comes to look on Man as no more than a complicated set of 'chubes', levers, articulations, pumps and pulleys, and other gadgets. In some very real senses the human body clearly *is* a machine. The dissecting room looks not unlike a motor-garage with pieces of machinery scattered about. But the bits can no longer be put together and made to work. The deadness in the place is a sobering influence, and one can't help wondering sometimes whether there is anything more to a corpse than that it once was alive, or anything more to oneself than that one will certainly someday be dead.

There used to be a saying, 'Show me three doctors and I'll show you two atheists.' When your job is to study the human machine, the things that go wrong with it, and the ways to put it right, there seems little point in bringing God into the picture, no more point than there would be for the motor-mechanic. The great mathematician, Laplace, is said to have replied, when asked why his scientific treatise made no mention of God, 'There was no need for that hypothesis.' For a working scientist that is a very proper line to take. Bringing God into the sequence, or network rather, of natural cause-and-effect only confuses the picture, and interferes with one's understanding of the processes concerned. The idea of God as an interfering magician is theologically naive, philosophically it is absurd, and scientifically it is wholly unrewarding. Yet there are some aspects of science where, if one surveys the whole field honestly, one must be led in my view to some sort of recognition of the fact of God, and to some appreciation of the nature of his creative work. One such field is that of the evolutionary development of man, of the species *Homo sapiens*. Man's evolution involves not only his own species, but also the evolutionary development of countless animal and plant forms without which Man as we know him could never have developed, and without which he could never survive. The end of the evolutionary process is Man. Its author is God.

Some of my scientific colleagues will object, of course, that this conclusion is not an impartial one; that I, who ask for integrity, am not looking at the matter wholly honestly. After all I have been a committed christian for a good deal longer, literally, than I can remember. I was baptised into the Catholic faith within days—hours almost—of my birth. That was in the early twenties, in a part of Lancashire where the Old Faith survived and even flourished in the Penal Days. So whatever *unconscious* memories I may have, of the time of my birth or the time before birth, or, according to Jungian theory, whatever race-memories might be stored in my little bit of the 'collective unconscious', I cannot have, as a 'cradle-Catholic', any *conscious* memories of what it is like *not* to be a christian. I have plenty of memories of what it is like at times to be a renegade christian—but that is a different state which raises its own problems. Now, if a scientific humanist objects that a christian has no right, if he is a scientist, to seek any correlation between his scientific and his religious knowledge, my reply is that this is the only thing he *can* do, if he is to be a man. Everyone has a framework or nexus of ideas, constructed out of past experiences, into which he incorporates whatever new observations and ideas come his way. We cannot escape wholly from these conditioning influences, and it is folly for a scientist to assume that he can—it is the silliest of follies if he further assumes, as some do, that *only the scientist* can escape from the trammels of past experience and be radically and wholly 'objective' about things. This is to try to put oneself outside nature. It is, perhaps, one sequel to nineteenth-century 'rationalism', so-called, to substitute Man, or rather his intellect, as a kind of man-made-God, a pseudo-God. It is essential, for thinking to be any good, that we should strive for absolute integrity and honesty in the effort. A claim to complete impartiality and objectivity, even about very matter-of-fact things, is bound to be in some senses dishonest because it is necessarily false.

As I have said, I cannot in the nature of things remember my baptism, my conversion to christianity. Adult conversions seem, from many accounts, to be experiences so rewarding that one is sometimes tempted to resent the fact that the submission and the promises were made for one, by godparents, at a time when one was completely unaware of what was going on. But of course, in so far as there is a difference between adult and infant baptism it is a difference at a purely *natural* level, psychological and emotional. The *supernatural* effects that stem from the grace of the sacrament are exactly the same, and these are the ones that really count. So far as the natural psychological experience goes one is free throughout life— only too free, alas—to know what it is like to be estranged from God, and to know what it is to turn back (be converted) to him. A christian is bound to find in life as much conflict as consolation—that is, if he tries to be comprehensive, 'catholic', in his thinking and his living.

I remember very well my first real discovery about God. It would count, I suppose, as a sort of 'first conscious conversion'. I was about eight years old at the time. At the church school, which I attended from the age of three, we were taught to raise our school caps on passing in front of the main doors of the parish church. Men did the same, and girls, ladies and capless boys were to bow the head. This wasn't at all a question, as might be thought at first sight, of saluting the Church itself. Rather it was an acknowledgment (according to Catholic doctrine) of the fact of the Real Presence of God on the altar. One would do no less on passing the Queen in front of Buckingham Palace, and the practice seemed perfectly natural and proper. I remember, at maybe seven or so, realising that since God could 'see out' through the doors both of the tabernacle and of the church, he could obviously see further, through houses as well. It would clearly, then, be correct and fitting to raise one's cap on passing any spot, in any street, which one judged would be opposite the front door of the church. I don't remember finding this in any way incongruous, even when the spot was outside a public house or a shop. Then the issue became rather more complicated (and perhaps this represented the beginning of my professional, anatomical interest in spacial relationships) when I realised that my childish image of God, looking through the front of the tabernacle, was quite inadequate. God clearly had no sides, and it was just as reasonable to raise one's cap on passing behind the church as it was on passing in front.

As I grew in knowledge and experience of the geography of other parish churches in the town (and there were a lot of them in Preston) the whole business, for a brief period in my life, assumed almost nightmarish proportions: I seemed to spend most of the day tipping my cap in the most unlikely places. And the thing was much too complicated, of course, to explain to any grown-ups who thought my behaviour a bit odd. And then, somehow, the solution to the nightmare came quite simply and quickly. The practice had nothing really to do with an outward display of courtesy and good manners, as I had supposed. It was all a matter of being reminded, in simple and homely fashion, that God is. Raising one's cap was an outward sign, it is true, but a sign of an inner thought that constituted a prayer. I ceased to worry about the rubric, and settled instead for the reminder and the prayer that went with it.

I suppose I have done much the same ever since. I tend to be critical of rules and rubrics in themselves, and try to see what they are there for. This sort of attitude has led me into many scrapes and conflicts, first in school, and later with Church authorities at various levels. I expect it will always be so with me. The real problem one has to face in any particular difficulty is 'am I working for God or against him?' It is never easy to answer. Self-will, self-interest, self-satisfaction, self-seeking, are powerful human forces. They can all too easily masquerade as 'independent thinking' or 'the voice of conscience'. Controlling these energies, and putting them at God's service rather than my own, constitutes for me one of the major tasks of life.

Broadcast in the BBC Overseas Service, 1964.

6

RELIGION AND BIOLOGICAL RESEARCH

The noise of the Victorian battle is heard today from afar off, and the 'thunder of the captains and the shouting' is somewhat dimmed with the passage of years and personalities. But he would be a bold man who would claim to have remained entirely unaffected by the legacy of emotional tension in the air, a tension which is, indeed, implicit in the matter. On the one hand we have the sense of mystery and personal inadequacy which is at the heart of all religion, and a wealth of poetic and religious imagery surrounding the little word 'life'. On the other are the avowed aims of biological research to render intelligible each and every manifestation of life; to explain the hitherto inexplicable; to bring the light of knowledge into the darkness of an ignorance which sometimes parades as innocence; to explore living matter at both the lowest and the highest levels, namely the structure of the protein molecules that form the physical basis of life, and the psychology of aesthetic and religious experience itself. Is there not bound to be unending strife—however polite might be the modern battle compared with that shooting war of the '60's and '70's—between two such radically different approaches of human beings towards the truth that is within and of themselves? And is not religion, with its content of the mysterious and its 'dark night of the soul', bound to find itself continually engaged in costly rearguard actions against the astonishing successes of modern biology and medicine, against each new discovery of 'natural' explanations for the most remarkable of vital phe-

nomena, against the piercing light now being cast both into
the depths of the human brain and psyche, and into the nature
of life itself? No one can afford a policy of indifference: in
affairs such as these we are all of us *engagés*.

The kind of buoyant scientific optimism to which we have
alluded comes relatively easily to the biological research-
worker—new observations and correlations are being published in ever-increasing abundance, and we know that as yet
we are only at the beginning of the history of this most complex of all the natural sciences: the future holds unlimited
promise. In a somewhat different fashion a faith in the future
advances of science was germane to the late nineteenth-
century ethos and, linked perhaps inevitably at the time with
militant agnosticism and a liberal-humanist philosophy, it
became a most potent force both in the world of the
professional scientist and on the socio-political 'front'. It is
sometimes said that in Western Europe today such 'scientific-
humanism' is a spent force, but in Cambridge at least this
seems not to be so, and unless Cambridge has taken over in
this matter the traditional role of Oxford, the fact of the local
movement is not without importance.

Since it was Darwin's biological bombshell in 1859 that
fanned the anti-clerical flames and gave such a boost to the
development of materialist philosophies of life, it might be of
advantage to try to pick out the significant points which under-
lay the controversy about 'Apes and Angels' as it was called—
the phrase is Disraeli's, and carries with it more of political
debating expediency than of philosophical or scientific exac-
titude. It is important to realise that Darwin's theory of the
gradual evolution of species from pre-existing forms was not
by any means a new one. But such had been the influence of
the great scientist Linnaeus in the latter part of the eighteenth
century, that attempts to deny his dogma of the immutability
of biological species were mostly decried as *scientifically* in-

admissible—until Darwin, that is, with a wealth of evidence
that no one could really hope to laugh out of court (though
Bishop Wilberforce, prompted by Professor Owen, did make
the attempt), swept the older idea to that well-populated
limbo where discarded scientific theories enjoy, let us hope,
their well-earned rest. At the beginning of the nineteenth
century this particular aspect of current biological theory inevitably favoured a literal interpretation of the relevant biblical passages and, perhaps even more significant in the event,
harmonised only too well with the philosophical deism so
prevalent in that machine-minded age. Such a vital synthesis
between Science, Philosophy and Religion is ever a powerful
force, is ever a rare phenomenon, and, up to the present at
least, has ever been short-lived. It could hardly be otherwise,
since new insight achieved by one member of the triumvirate
requires adjustment by the others at a speed faster than they
are likely to find possible: it is never easy to assess at first sight
whether an adjustment will remain marginal or prove to be
central to the subject—easiest, perhaps, in the natural sciences,
but even there conservatism is a potent restraining force.

The deism of the previous century had found one of its
ablest exponents in Archdeacon Paley of the famous 'watch'
analogy, and new editions of his works were still appearing
with great regularity. On reading today his book on *Natural
Theology* one cannot but marvel in some respects, not only at
the intrinsic beauty of the language and the author's obvious
delight in all of nature's wonders, but also at his calm and
confident marshalling of the 'facts' as they appeared to him.
One sees him construct for himself that great universal watch,
of which the design he perceived in nature spoke to him so
eloquently of a Great Designer (Architect, Mathematician,
Planner—how many and how remote are the appellations
used of the Inexpressible by deist thinkers!). The Omnipotent
Manufacturer of the Perfect Machine, this was God in the

immediate pre-Darwinian era, the Designer who planned, about 6,000 years ago, every structural and functional detail of the birds of the air, the beasts of the field, and Man to be Lord of Creation. It is not surprising if to the imagination this eminently transcendent master-mind should present itself as a venerable but rather frightening old man, wearing a beard and looking somewhat like Alfred Lord Tennyson (or perhaps Karl Marx, as has been remarked)—there can be few of us, even today, who have not been to some extent affected, and correspondingly impoverished, by this pious nursery picture of the Divine Spirit. If we had happened to belong to a different zoological class we should undoubtedly, at this level of thinking, see him as

> Immense, of fishy form and mind,
> squamous, omnipotent and kind.

What the scientist wanted was to be rid of his own outdated theory (which in fact was no theory at all—not in the scientific sense), and with it its accumulated wrappings of superficial philosophy and loose unscholarly biblical exegesis. Unfortunately, out with the bath-water went a very real baby, and it is only in comparatively recent years that some workers have come across the infant once again. A baby, like any other biological organism, is very much a living, breathing unity, and an integrated creature of this sort can be properly studied only 'in the flesh' as we say: if you first put it to death and take it to pieces you will be studying no longer an 'organism' but a number of rather different things. Yet such studies were both inevitable and necessary once the idea of organic evolution had caught the scientific imagination and inspired the search for 'evidences'. While a great deal, clearly, was to be gained in the process, much too was to be lost, and the effects of the loss are still felt to some extent in the world of biology today. The reasons for the biologists' temporary flight from *bios* to *thanatos* are instructive. For one thing men did not at all

abandon the idea of a mechanical universe simply because the
design of the machine seemed not to be as sound as had been
thought; rather was cartesian mechanism strengthened by
the new theories, but now it was Blind Chance that produced
and modified biological organisms, instead of the Deity of
earlier theorisers, for whom, of course, modifications had been
out of the question. It is something of a mystery why Churchmen of the period allowed themselves to be so stampeded by
the turn of scientific events: the real 'argument from design'
loses none of its force simply because *human* purpose cannot
everywhere be perceived, and indeed, by the discovery of each
and every natural scientific law the argument is strengthened,
not weakened; further, the far more cogent 'argument from
contingency' was never even called in question. The wholly
transcendent deity with the beard must have been at the time
a powerful image in the clerical psyche. However that may be,
the average biologist (and many above-average, although one
speaks of course in generalities, ignoring many for whom
science and religion were always complementary) came
to think of living creatures as *nothing more than* complex
machines, determined by chance, and operating solely according to the laws of Newtonian physics and chemistry. Now the
logical way to study a machine is to take it to pieces and
examine its component parts. Unhappily, in biology such
treatment is literally fatal, and must be offset, if truth is to be
safeguarded, by study of the whole creature as a living unity,
as it usually had been in pre-Darwinian days. For a time, however, biology belied its name, and many academic exponents
of the subject became no more than museum-experts, constructing theories about life from a study of death. That sorry,
if necessary, phase was still in vogue within living memory,
but clearly it could not continue indefinitely, and experiments
with living things were bound gradually to supersede the old
dead morphology: already for some time 'physiology' had

been regarded as a subject quite distinct from 'anatomy'. The modern research-worker is not always sufficiently conscious, however, of the debt he owes to the descriptive morphologists of the past—indeed he sometimes tends, in his ignorance, to disparage their work as unworthy of the intellects engaged in it. He does not always appreciate, perhaps, that the very theory of organic evolution, which lies at the heart of modern biology and conditions all our thinking on the subject, a theory which has affected, indeed, almost every sphere of modern thought, was secured and established largely by the comparative anatomists. If, with the almost total victory (after some vicissitudes) of evolutionary theory, we cannot all of us now feel the urge to continue the same sort of exacting enquiries pursued by those giants, yet we would be lacking in proper historical sense if we failed to appreciate the reasons for their morphological enthusiasms, lacking in charity if we failed to recognise the immense debt we owe them—not only for the theoretical significance of their work but also for that vast store of factual information on which we draw continually—and lacking in human understanding if we tried to minimise the work of those who, even today, want to see for themselves, and are not above using their eyes to see with. There are always many more questions to ask of nature than there are answers available, and for all its impressiveness the nineteenth century only scratched the surface of significant morphological enquiry.

But concentration upon the anatomy of the parts of the machine tended towards (again one speaks in generalisations) an attitude of pure materialism, a philosophy enhanced still more when physiological theories as to the functioning of the machine were expressed, as was again inevitable, in mechanistic terms. Analysis and specialisation, those ever-growing twins of science, are bound to be mechanically-minded. To the scientist it *need* only be when physical analysis has been pushed to its furthest limits, as perhaps in some branches of modern physics, that there reappears a positive need for philosophy as a subject in its own right. But the modern revolution in physics has as yet had virtually no effect on biological theory, and in this sphere Newton still reigns supreme. It is in the nature of things that no sort of spiritual principle can possibly emerge from analysis of physical morphology, nor from its expression in terms of natural function—whether the terms used be physiological, psychological, biochemical or biophysical makes little difference. If one is naive enough to go looking for some sort of spiritual element with a microscope or an electrical potentiometer one will be either disappointed or satisfied, according to one's purpose and to the sort of philosophy one brings to the laboratory bench. The physical sciences are concerned only to explain natural phenomena in terms of material and efficient causes, and use techniques designed for the purpose. In so far as biology has been conceived of as nothing more than the physical (at a level, of course, of extraordinary complexity) the investigator has automatically chosen appropriate techniques of investigation. But if you go to nature's shop prepared to buy only in copper currency you cannot expect to get very precious things in return (though nature often gives extraordinarily good measure); it may be that for real insight into the organisation of living creatures the coinage needs to be of finer metal. He was a wise supervisor who first gave that best-of-all advice to the biological research-student, 'Young man, be very careful what you look for, because you are sure to find it.' There is a real sense in which for the biologist at least, analytical researches in increasingly-specialised fields are inherently restrictive; for so long as biology continued to develop by processes of ramification and diversification, then, despite the vast increase in factual knowledge made available, some debasement of the currency of biological theory was perhaps inevitable.

This brief survey of the development of that biological materialism which forms so powerful a factor in the general materialism of our age should logically be followed, first by discussion of the various attempts that have been made to resolve the very real dilemma we posed at the beginning of this article, and then by exposition of what one believes oneself to be the correct approach towards achieving the desired synthesis, without the sacrifice of either religious or scientific integrity. Space does not here permit such a discussion at the level which the subject warrants, and it is proposed, in conclusion, merely to observe that the materialist 'heresy' might perhaps be crumbling within the science of biology itself. The modern outlook, wherever it has developed, is characterised by an increasingly-felt need to synthesise and co-ordinate. The trend is evidenced by two quite distinct features. Firstly, it is becoming increasingly difficult to classify a great deal of current biological research as belonging to any one of the 'traditional' subdivisions of a University Faculty of Biology—if three-quarters of a century can be considered long enough for the establishment of 'traditions'. Research techniques and interests now straddle the old departmental divisions with a fine disregard for places and people, a fact which leads to some curious anomalies in the academic life. Secondly, there is a return to the study of the creature no longer in terms solely of its parts, but once again as a living unity: the trend is seen, for instance, in zoology in the growth of the subject called 'animal behaviour', and in medicine, where above all the concept should never have been lost, in the growing realisation of the significance of what is called, not altogether happily, 'psychosomatic medicine'—the very term is indicative of the former disruption. Subjects of this kind require the development of new scientific techniques, no longer restricted to terms of Newtonian physics and chemistry, but techniques which are curiously and properly 'biological' in nature. What the change

Religion and Biological Research

might lead to cannot in any sense be foreseen, but one ventures to suggest that the science of biology might become emancipated from the old philosophy of crude materialism—against which the internal reaction was an equally crude vitalism—and will begin to be 'holistic' in outlook. There is nothing in modern biology which can be construed as essentially antireligious in the way that the materialist philosophy must be. Of course, it might well happen that there will develop a series of *new* biological heresies which orthodox religion will have to face. It would be remarkable if there did not. But at least it will be a change.

The Cambridge Review, 1956, vol. 77, pp. 383-5.

7

CATHOLICS AND THE DARWIN CENTENARY

Many and varied have been the books on evolution published in recent months to celebrate the centenary of the Darwin-Wallace communications to the Linnaean Society concerning their theory of evolution by Natural Selection. It was the stimulus provided by Darwin's theories of the *mechanisms* of the evolutionary process which led to the general adoption, in the nineteenth century, of the much wider and more fundamental notion that biological evolution has actually occurred, and that all living creatures are part of the process.

The idea that a process of gradual evolution might account for the observable diversity of living forms has a history as old as the recorded history of human thought. The philosophical and theological implications of this idea, as contrasted with its only alternative, the idea of the 'special creation' of each of the countless numbers of recognisable 'species' that now exist and of the far more numerous 'species' that once existed and are now extinct, have been debated by christian writers ever since the time of the Fathers. There is no question, for instance, that to St Augustine, with his concept of seminal ratios, the notion of the special creation of things as a way of accounting for their coming into being was quite unacceptable, even absurd. But until comparatively recently the idea of evolution was essentially a speculative one, a theory concerning which reasonable men might justifiably differ in their conclusions. If special creationism seemed to some a most unlikely way for divine Providence to act in the world, yet in the absence of definite evidence to the contrary it was clearly an alternative possibility, and one which allowed for a literal reading of the account of creation given in Genesis. The situation so far as the science of biology was concerned was much the same as had been that in speculative astronomy during the time, before Galileo, when the Ptolemaic and Copernican theories were debated as alternatives, with the balance of evidence favouring the Ptolemaic account.

What Galileo did for Copernican astronomy, Charles Darwin did for evolutionary biology. Immediately before Darwin's time the vast majority of biologists, schooled in the tradition of Linnaeus and Cuvier, had joined with non-scientific philosophers and theologians in accepting as fact the Linnaean dogma of the fixity of species, and hence of the doctrine of special creation as the only conceivable way of accounting for their existence. After the publication of Darwin's careful observations on the degrees of diversity of biological forms and his theories to account for them by a process of 'modification by descent', the final vindication of the general theory of evolution was assured.

In the century that has followed, and particularly in the last twenty-five years, quite remarkable advances have been made in our understanding of the nature of the evolutionary process, and we see that Darwin in fact was often more right than were the 'Darwinists' who followed him and who popularised certain aspects of his work. Darwin's genius as a scientist and his capacity for achieving high levels of abstract conceptual reasoning while nevertheless giving full weight to those facts which he patiently collected throughout his professional life, are today becoming more and more apparent. His place amongst that select company that includes Newton and Einstein is now beyond question.

The British Academy 'Lecture on a Master Mind' for 1958

was devoted to Charles Darwin, and was delivered by Sir Gavin de Beer. The observation was there made that 'scarcely a day passes without the appearance of new evidence confirming the truth of the theory of evolution up to the hilt, and it is now universally accepted except by those who are too ignorant or too idle to acquaint themselves with the facts, or too obsessed by irrational considerations to follow scientific evidence wherever it may lead.' There must be quite a lot of Catholics, readers perhaps of this article, who will either cringe under the lash of such criticism or who will be driven by it to even further extremes of so-called 'rationalisation' in self-justification.

But let them not despair, either of themselves or of pontificating scientists. There has recently been published on this subject a careful and well-balanced book[1] in the Pelican series. For a total financial outlay of three shillings and sixpence (the intellectual outlay will be heavier since the book merits, demands indeed, many hours of close and concentrated study), it is now open to all to 'acquaint themselves with the facts' at least. Cases involving obsession with 'irrational considerations' are, of course, more difficult to treat.

The book is no light-hearted popular account of the subject. The author took a first degree in engineering, and has brought to his professional studies in biology a penetrating mind that delights in the exactitudes of mechanics and mathematics. He warns his lay-readers in advance: 'Before starting a formal training in biology, I had read a number of books about evolution, some intended primarily for specialists and some for laymen. Although there were always, in the former kind, passages which I could not follow, I found such books more satisfying than those written for laymen, since in the latter I had always the feeling that difficulties were being slurred over. I have tried to avoid this fault. Although I have not assumed

1. Smith, John Maynard, *The Theory of Evolution*, Penguin, London, 1958.

any specialized knowledge in the reader, and when possible have drawn my examples from familiar animals and plants, I have not omitted any subjects merely because they are difficult.'

It is no longer profitable or even possible to discuss evolutionary theory in the general terms that were used in the nineteenth and early twentieth centuries. The reader of this book must be prepared, with due assistance from the author, to grapple with technical terms such as *allotetraploid*, *heterosis*, *phenotype* and *translocation*, to mention but a few. He must also be ready to follow the mathematical reasoning involved in studies of changes in population-structure, and to understand that different factors will be involved as between a community which is small and isolated and one which is large and freely inter-breeding. Evolutionary trends and possibilities are markedly affected by such matters, and they are of the utmost significance for students of *human* evolution. But this book contains very little of the evidence for evolutionary trends in our own species—the author has quite properly devoted himself to those aspects of evolutionary theory for which experimental and statistical evidence is fairly complete and correspondingly compelling. While it is inevitable that scientific understanding of each and every process that has occurred during two thousand million years of biological evolution will always be incomplete, and hence open to attack on specific points, yet the positive evidence concerning the underlying causes of biological modifications and of their retention or rejection by the sieve of natural selection is so strong, that he would have to be a curiously irrational reader who failed to give to the modern account a fair degree of credence.

It should be recorded that Maynard Smith commits himself with scarcely any reserve to the orthodox and rather rigid school of so-called 'neo-Darwinian' genetical theory. It is true that members of this school have, with a certain amount of justification, called themselves exponents of a 'modern synthesis'. And yet scientific observations have recently been made which cannot, it would seem, be accommodated within the strictly neo-Darwinian nexus of hypothesis and theory. The author leaves out of account those experimental findings which indicate that modifications induced in animal cells during ontogeny (i.e. so-called 'acquired characters') are in fact, in some instances at least, incorporated into the genetic make-up and handed on to future generations. Perhaps he felt that these findings were too recent to justify inclusion in a book of this sort. But one has the feeling that in his discussion (p. 50 ff.) of 'Nature and Nurture' he mentions the possibility of such reactions only in order to dismiss them as highly unlikely, as any orthodox neo-Darwinian must. Darwin himself would not have done so, and it may well be that the next decade or two will see those aspects of Lamarckism which Darwin found acceptable becoming once again scientifically respectable. This will lead to the development of a synthesis of hypotheses at a higher level of generality, a process typical of scientific advance.

It is a matter for considerable puzzlement, and deep regret, that at a time when evolutionary theory is making such tremendous strides in the world of the professional biologist, the subject is regarded with such suspicion and even open hostility by so many Catholics in this country. It is undeniable that in recent years evolution has had rather a 'bad press' in English Catholic newspapers and periodicals, much worse than in any other group of publications—though of course there is always a lunatic fringe hovering around any community. Recent treatment in the Catholic press compares so unfavourably with what appears to have been the case more than fifty years ago that one's sense of bewilderment increases.

Catholic opposition to the scientific theory cannot derive basically from philosophical or theological objections for, as was said above, St Augustine, and before him St Gregory of Nyssa, would have seen the theory as an eminently reasonable one. The metaphysical and theological need to speak of a 'Creator and Sustainer of all things' is in no sense in conflict with the natural scientist's urge to discover and describe *how* effects come about in nature. The fact that the theory of evolution has been developed and expounded with great force by avowed atheists and agnostics has little bearing on the validity of the scientific findings themselves. But perhaps some of our Catholic activists feel an urge, when they read an article by a prominent agnostic dealing ostensibly with his professional scientific work but in a manner highly charged with philosophical overtones, to refute not merely the anti-theological background to the article but the facts of the subject-matter themselves? They would do well to ponder the advice of St Augustine, in *De Genesi ad litteram* lib. I cap XIX, on the need to avoid this type of criticism. Much the same view was expressed by Mgr J. A. O'Brien in the preface to his book *Evolution and Religion* (N.Y. 1931). Criticising some of the writings on this subject 'from the pens of religious leaders', he says: 'They have been largely concerned with minimizing the force of the scientific evidence, playing upon occasional disagreements among the scientists concerning details in the converging lines of evidence—details usually inconsequential in their bearing upon the fundamental issue—and in general seeking to cast discredit upon the data presented and, at times, even ridicule upon those presenting the same.' It is this type of cheap and ineffective (except to the unlearned) criticism that brings the Church into disrepute in those circles where the calm search for and appraisal of objective truth are regarded as amongst the highest of human aspirations.

It is noteworthy that in the quarrel of last century between certain agnostic scientists and the churchmen of the period, Catholic clergymen were not by any means always to be found deep in the reactionary ranks. David Lack, in his book *Evolutionary Theory and Christian Belief* (1957) writes: 'So far as I am aware the first substantial and sympathetic appraisal of animal evolution by an ecclesiastic was that in the *Dublin Review* for 1871 by the Roman Catholic Canon Hedley.' That essay, together with a commentary by Abbot Butler on it and on some later writings on evolution by Bishop Hedley, was reprinted in book form in 1931. The story is there told by Abbot Butler of the opposition to the bishop's position from some ecclesiastical quarters. A fuller account of a curious history, in which a further step was taken by the recent Pope when he admitted at least the possibility of 'the development, from other living matter already in existence, of the human body', was given by Dr E. C. Messenger in his *Evolution and Theology* (1932) and its sequel, *Theology and Evolution* (1949). The late Dr Messenger was also responsible for the English translation of Canon Dorlodot's *Darwinism and Catholic Thought* (1922) in which is recounted the tremendous effect made in 1909 by Dorlodot when, as representative of the Catholic University of Louvain, he gave his laudatory address to the Cambridge congress that was celebrating the centenary of Darwin's birth. Messenger commented that the 'address sounded just the right note in the opinion of all the Catholics present, and was subsequently given publicity in the *Tablet*.' Forty-nine years later a much larger International Congress of Zoology met in London to celebrate the centenary of Darwin's first publication on evolution. There was nothing comparable, so far as Catholics were concerned, to the events of half a century previously.

Perhaps the reason for the apparent regress of Catholic appreciation in this country of this particular branch of science is to be found in the history of the development of evolutionary theory itself. After the rediscovery, at the turn of the century, of Mendel's work on heredity, there slowly developed a deep cleavage amongst professional biologists as to the principal agent concerned in the evolutionary process. The two camps comprised the 'old-fashioned' Darwinian selectionists and the 'up-to-date' Mendelian geneticists. For a good many years the Darwinists had rather a bad time of it, and during the 1920's a great deal of 'good Catholic fun' was to be had by the Chester-belloc and its followers by quotation of isolated statements from different scientists who clearly failed to see eye to eye both as to fact and its interpretation. Absurdities abounded and were gleefully exposed. Unhappily there are some Catholics today who are still unaware, it would seem, that these scientific contradictions and disagreements were resolved nearly thirty years ago. The new era was ushered in with a book by Professor Sir Ronald Fisher with the fitting title *The Genetical Theory of Selection* (Oxford 1930). The earlier disputes have long since passed into the history of the development of modern biological theory, and their place has been taken by others as indicated above. But there are still to be found Catholic writers who are prepared to quote from the giants and dwarfs of the past as if their views bore direct relevance to the scientific issues of today.

If there should be any readers of this article who, hesitant about the validity of the general theory of evolution, find themselves familiar only with pre-1930 versions of the theory, they would, unhappily but necessarily, qualify for the first half of the stricture quoted above from de Beer's British Academy lecture. One hopes they might acquire the new book by Maynard Smith. And read it.

The Month, 1959, vol. 207, pp. 301-7.

8

MEDICAL SCIENTISTS AND THE VIEW
THAT HISTORY IS BUNK

A paper read in the University of California, Los Angeles, 1966

I am grateful for this opportunity to address the Los Angeles Society for the History of Medical Science. Particularly am I grateful to you, Mr President, for agreeing so readily to my somewhat provocative title. I speak, of course, not as a professional historian, but as a practising medical scientist. I am proud to belong to this relatively new scientific group, one which is growing apace in the bosom of—I must not say the oldest profession—but at any rate one of the oldest. However, despite my enthusiasm for my chosen field, I shall be saying hard things tonight, as my title might suggest, about some aspects of current medical science. Publicly to criticise any part of the medical profession, which must constitute one of the most powerful trade unions in the world, is a politically dangerous game. I can think of some medical audiences where I should have to choose my words with infinite care and tact, and not merely to avoid the social solecism of giving offence to hosts. Here in Los Angeles, however, and particularly in these buildings, I feel curiously secure, and relieved that I can speak my mind freely and without constraint in defence of the scholarly pursuit of medical history. After all, where else in the academic world would one find two Professors of the History of Medicine who also happen to hold office respectively as Chancellor and Dean of Graduate Studies? I like to think of this happy circumstance as a symptom rather than a cause of the respect for Medical History that I have found at

U.C.L.A. So if my talk tonight is bound to offend some—and that is the inevitable price one pays for selecting provocative subjects—it may be there will be others in the audience who will give it a sympathetic hearing. To those who are about to be offended I can only offer condolences in advance, and express the hope that my remarks, however annoying, won't seem altogether too outrageous. I would particularly ask you to remember that my experience and conclusions are the product of my membership of four universities in Britain. Any resemblance to local personnel or practice is entirely coincidental.

The view that History is Bunk was first enunciated, in so many words, by a very successful citizen of this country, Henry Ford I. If he was the first with sufficient courage to say it openly he was surely not the first, nor the last, to feel it. This has been the view of the practical man down the ages. For a motor-car manufacturer, or a plumber, say, it is a very understandable position. What good is the past to anyone for whom only the present and the future can present a challenge? Indeed this attitude is to be commended in a technological consultant, that is if one is simply concerned with trouble-free combustion engines, or with water-closets that will work as one wants them to. It will be my contention tonight that the present period of flowering of medical science will see re-enacted, though in different form, that struggle of over three hundred years ago, between the physicians and the barber-surgeons. The medical profession has now acquired—but only very recently—the right and the freedom to choose between a future as skilled barbers, plumbers, general repair men, and/or a future as men of learning and understanding, fit to take their place in a community of scholars. The two prospects open to us are not by any means necessarily incompatible. Moreover I want to insist at the outset that I have the highest regard for plumbers and barbers, especially skilled ones. But I happen also to think that the medical profession properly belongs in the universities. It has something to contribute to, and something to gain from the academic *milieu*, that would be lost if medicine were pursued, as once it was, and as plumbing still is pursued, in trade schools or technical colleges, or by a system of apprenticeship to successful practitioners of the craft.

It isn't easy to define just what this 'something' is. It is certainly true that the art and science of medicine can be and often are taught and practised in relative isolation from the rest of the academic community. Even in the best-run universities this is what always tends to happen. It takes a positive effort, by those who think it important enough to make the effort, to stop the medical members of staff and their pupils from forming an isolated group, concerned exclusively with their own affairs and their own advancement. Traditionally the medical clique is reluctant to talk anything but shop. It constitutes a group, therefore, from which the *non-cognoscenti* are necessarily excluded because of the sheer weight of technical jargon employed. Now, I ask myself, why should this be so? I do not accept the theory that the phenomenon, which is well-recognised by our non-medical colleagues, represents a kind of intellectual narcissism, and indicates an academic immaturity amongst medical men, who are then forced to rely on hocus-pocus and the gullibility of the public for the maintenance of self-respect and a high income-level. True, one may occasionally come across a kind of medical fossil who holds to the pre-scientific view that the medical art (not science, for living fossils hardly recognise its existence) needs to be surrounded by an aura of mystery in order to be effective. The general public knows full well that medicine today can and should be approached scientifically. They know too that it is of the essence of science that it is open to any honest enquiry and welcomes it. The public expects, and has a right to demand, that medical men will answer their questions, and will speak the truth even if, as things now stand, it may mean the 'don't know' response much more often than one would like. The days of mystique in medicine are surely, if not quite over, at least numbered. With that will go all the self-opinionated pomposity and complacency that were characteristic of many members of the profession, say, in Victorian times.

Now in the dark days of mystery-medicine doctors were generally much more conscious of the long, colourful and significant history of the profession than we are today. In saying this I am laying an easy trap for myself. The 'switched-on' modern doctor, surrounded by diagnostic and therapeutic instruments of the most ingenious complexity, might testily reply: 'Exactly. History and mystery always go together. Both are bunk, and we should be glad to be shot of them.' It is interesting, in scientific laboratories today, to observe the curious reaction of the group when one of its members displays a real interest in the history of his subject, or in the philosophical presuppositions that underlie his experimental procedures. It is conceivable that his whim might be treated indulgently by his colleagues, provided he is already a Nobel Laureate. But privately they will be liable even then to talk of him somewhat pityingly as having 'gone off the boil', or being 'over the hump', or even as 'going round the bend'. For a relatively young man to show such anti-group, nonconformist traits in the laboratory is enough, in some places, to nip his career in the bud. It is like an aspiring executive in modern advertising daring to ask searching questions about the real merits and background of the products he is called upon to promote. I would be risking quite a lot, I can assure you, in speaking as I do now, were it not for the fact that my Cambridge career has reached that happy point where I can afford to say almost anything I like to almost anybody I like. That is when the phrase 'academic freedom' finally becomes meaningful. Once one has tasted it one doesn't want to lose it again by becoming too much of a target for pressures exerted by conflicting forces.

In Cambridge there are many reminders of history. In the context of this talk I will speak of only one. When one assumes office as a member of the academic staff, or 'faculty' as you would say, one formally accepts certain obligations. These are laid down in the statutes of the university, which are rarely altered because that requires the approval of Her Majesty in Council on the basis of a university petition, which itself is the outcome of long debates and an elaborate system of voting by the 'faculty'. The statutes lay down, amongst other things, that it shall be the duty of the officer to promote the welfare and interests of the university, and in particular its four specific aims, which are listed as Education, Religion, Learning and Research. Now that may have a rather old-fashioned ring. Many scholars would certainly baulk, for instance, at the idea of being called upon to promote religion. For myself I can accept even that obligation as part of university life provided that the word religion is permitted to carry only its classical meaning, that of a 'binding' or 'commitment'. It doesn't matter in this context to what particular cause or set of ideas a man commits himself, provided that the commitment is properly thought through, is open to free discussion and analysis within the community, and is conscientiously adhered to until something sufficiently important happens to lead to an honest change of allegiance. It has been the universities' failure to have anything worthwhile or meaningful to say about commitment that has led to the current mood of disenchantment with the system amongst undergraduates on lively campuses. I look on most of these reactions as welcome clinical evidence of viability in what one had begun to suspect was almost moribund. I understand that the same sort of things have been happening in this country recently.

What of the other three university aims? Only the last, of

course, Research, is held in high regard in this curious culture of ours. There are many reasons why this should be so, mostly obvious, and mostly to do with the age-old business of the acquisition of wealth and power. These are aims which are laudable enough, to be sure, in moderation. But their current inflation, or escalation, is surely at the root of the catastrophic decline in recent decades in the pursuit of other traditional academic aims. There comes a point when Research—with a capital R—can justly be regarded, in my view, as a corrupting influence in an academic community. I hope I have no need to declare that I am not, as Jowett of Balliol was, against research in the university. Far from it. But it has recently assumed a status and importance in the academic ship which has produced such a list to starboard that if we don't do something soon we might capsize altogether. Jowett envisaged this development, or collapse rather, a century ago.

So far as the aim of Education is concerned, it is difficult, in a university medical school, to escape it altogether—though we all know people who try (sometimes with success) to do just that. One cannot really blame them, if one examines the total situation objectively and dispassionately. Because of the current inflation (in every connotation of the word, people, things, money, status, motivation, publicity) of Research in the university economy there is only one reward given today to anyone who displays real ability, and expends real effort, in the field of teaching. That is the personal satisfaction to be got from knowing that one has communicated something worthwhile to one's pupils, and done it effectively. There is satisfaction, too, in receiving from them as a result a measure of respect and gratitude, and from watching their subsequent careers develop in ways to which one has in part contributed. These things make up in some degree for the emotional deprivation that results from a doctor's decision to give up clinical work in order to pursue basic medical science. Now emotion has no cash value, and it is in any case a highly personal and somewhat unpredictable benefit. Nevertheless as things stand now it is the only reward that a faculty member can hope for if he really exerts himself to some purpose in the interests of his undergraduate pupils. Research students are, of course, quite a different matter. They ought to get their motivation and inspiration in undergraduate classes, where today, unfortunately, they often get the very opposite of those desirable stimuli. In the present situation one might even think it prudent to advise an aspiring entrant to the academic profession not to give any hint, on first appointment, that he has any genuine talent or liking for teaching. Because if he does he will (a) get more of it than he really wants or can afford, being pressed into service by older colleagues who have learned very well which side of the academic bread is buttered these days; (b) he may very likely have to face a growing realisation in time that in some subtle way (and sometimes not so subtle) he is despised by those same colleagues who are grateful for the burdens he bears; and (c) his promotion up the academic ladder is likely to be very slow indeed.

Now it is true that a man may be excellent at research and utterly hopeless as a teacher. Only one of these two attributes (of excellence and hopelessness) has any value, but people sometimes try to make a virtue out of necessity and pretend that both are desirable in the form stated. The converse, however (excellence in teaching, hopelessness in research), I do not think is ever found, at any rate not if one is thinking of teaching at a proper university level. I have never known a really good university teacher, let alone a brilliant one (rare specimens these days), who was not also an original and creative thinker with a lively and flexible mind. He has to have these attributes in order to keep up with his really bright pupils, and to keep them interested in his subject. Of course, if the nature and content of university teaching and examining is reduced to hack-work, involving nothing more than a reasonably good memory, then any hack teacher (or hack computer one should add today) might meet the requirements adequately. But then we are not talking of *The Idea of a University* as conceived by John Henry Newman, or indeed by anyone who has had the time and energy, the intelligence and necessary insight to think deeply about the basic question, 'what are universities really for?'

But we are not so much concerned, tonight, with the first two of the aims to which, as a Cambridge don, I am by statute bound, but rather with the third, namely Learning. This has suffered immeasurably in recent years, and evidences of its lack are beginning to show themselves in many places. Now to me, Learning is the only specifically and uniquely human activity that we have so far mentioned. Other animal species are capable of acquiring information, they have their rules of behaviour or 'commitments', and they engage in exploration or research. Now all Learning, properly understood, is historical. Only man, so far as we know, is capable of appreciating and understanding history, or even of knowing that there is any such thing. It follows that to ignore history is to be less than human. We *are* our history. Whatever we do we are conditioned and moulded by that inescapable fact. When in research-work we gain some new insight, see a little further, it is well to remember, as some of our predecessors did, that we break through a cloud here and there only because we are 'standing on the shoulders of giants'. How many of us today, in the hurly-burly of experimentation, ever give more than a nod in the direction of the giants of the past? 'No time,' is the excuse, 'there's a grant to be got, a publication-priority to establish, a prize or a promotion to be aimed for.' The blinkers are on, the view is narrowed, and the horizon comes closer and closer. Intellectual myopia is surely the occupational disease of the moment of medical researchers. We are of the age of advertising, ready to believe implicitly that what is new is necessarily better. Our only therapeutic hope is the revival of Learning as a basic and wholly praiseworthy pursuit of academics. I look forward to the day when it is again possible to speak to one's colleagues of something quite new to them, and significant for their work, without feeling embarrassed about having to add, 'but of course this isn't really new. It was all described by so-and-so more than a century ago.' As of today there is nothing more certain to kill interest in an idea than the information that it is not a neonate. One can almost feel the drop in attention-level. We have accepted the journalists' outlook that what is not new is not newsworthy and what is not newsworthy is of no interest.

I should explain, perhaps, what I mean by Learning, and why I apply it to human behaviour specifically. After all, many psychologists and animal-behaviourists talk of 'learning processes' in other species. They do so in a sense which tends, I think, to devalue the word. Linguistic matters can only be tackled by enquiring how words are used. When we talk of a 'man of learning' or a 'learned man', we mean something much more than that this individual has a considerable amount of factual information permanently stored and at his complete disposal. If this were not the case we should have to reckon as the most learned of all those curious individuals who can store and repeat at will incredible sequences of numbers or 'facts' of any sort. Yet they make their living, or used to, by doing music-hall appearances, not by being consulted as learned men. In general, species other than man, including computing machines, are much more dependent on, limited to, and confined by the static information-content they have acquired. Storing facts, collecting data, are not by any means specifically human activities. What really matters is how one handles them. For too many scientists today data-collecting has taken the place of stamp-collecting as an agreeable way of passing the time—especially agreeable since you can actually get paid for doing it these days. The majority of the papers that flood the scientific journals today are little more than catalogues of data-collections, very dull and quite indigestible—or at any rate quite undigested by those who proffer them. Readers, of course, know them to be dull, and take appropriate action. Some 'research-communications' never succeed in communicating anything to anyone. Have you ever had that strange feeling, when submitting a paper for publication, that once it has got past the editorial board nobody (not even, these days, a human type-compositor), is ever going to read any of it apart from the summary? Requests for reprints tell one nothing these days, except that the paper has 'reached the charts' (no value-judgements involved!) in some abstracting service, and that some secretary perhaps has standing instructions to send for all papers on certain subjects. The proof of the hypothesis comes when your paper is quoted in a list of references by an author whose text clearly shows that he either hasn't read it, or hasn't understood it.

Everybody engaged in scientific medicine recognises that the publication-explosion (beside which the population-explosion seems a very slow-moving affair) has produced a crisis-situation. And yet, because of the power of the established system, we go on adding daily to the source of the crisis. We are slowly drowning in a sea of print; consumed, as I have heard it put, in our own excrement. We all know that the situation is intolerable. Why then do we go on tolerating it? The editorial board of one learned journal in England did its bit by changing the last of the questions put to those specialists who referee the papers submitted for publication. The old form of the question was, 'Do you see any reason why this paper should not be published in the Journal of so-and-so?' They decided they would simply leave out the word 'not'. So the question now reads, 'Do you see any reason why this paper should be published etc. ?' I am told that there has been quite a remarkable increase in rejection-rates, and that as a result the delay between submission and publication has been reduced to less than half what it was. This may have helped the individual journal to solve its own domestic problems, but it doesn't begin to touch the larger issue. Many publishers are business-men primarily, who know that they can hardly lose at the moment on promoting new journals. Sales are virtually guaranteed. They have made sure that *any* scientific paper can find some sort of home, however humble. Some seem to find half a dozen, and thereby add to the confusion and quite in-digestible bulk of the 'literature', as we still have the temerity to call it. Is it any wonder that the modern scientist, finding himself unable to keep up with even the current papers in his field, should find little enthusiasm for historical reading? When a pre-1920 paper does manage to creep into the so-called (often rather fraudulently so) 'historical introduction' that editors still seem to like, if only for appearances' sake, it is interesting to see, if the field is a popular one, how often it will be quoted within a year or two. This happens even when there are far better papers by the same author dating from the same period. I have sometimes thought of putting in a deliberate mistake to see how long it might survive. The phenomenon illustrates, I think, what we all suspect anyway to be true, namely that the fact that an author quotes a paper, even though he manages to get the reference correct, is no guarantee that he has actually read it. It is the crisis-situation that leads to the development of these forms of petty cheating. That in itself would be of minor consequence, except that meanwhile vast areas of established knowledge, careful observations and in-genious, well-tested scientific laws and hypotheses, are simply lost to modern researchers. We excuse ourselves by saying that every generation has to discover things afresh for itself. Thereby we reject that one feature that makes human evolution different in kind from all that went before it, namely the ability not merely to know, but to know that one knows, and to know how to transmit knowledge, culture and power (whether inherited or acquired) down the ages, so that their effects really do become cumulative.

And yet what are we to do in the face of library shelves to which acres of printed pages are added daily? One approach to this truly Herculean task (from a phrase I used earlier you will appreciate that I am thinking of Hercules and the Augean stables) that is being tried in many centres is to make over all published works to computer-programmers for abstracting and indexing. The mind reels. It won't be long before someone, I suppose, gets a very large grant in order to transfer all the trivia from the daily press on to tape or punched cards. I have known sensitive thinking scientists who have secretly dreaded the idea that their hard-won contributions would end up as footnotes in textbooks. Now we may all end up as punched cards. The proposed system will help to provide us with even longer lists of references. But who will help us find the tiny grains of salt in all that dough?

But we should have faith in human ingenuity. We should hope and expect that we shall eventually find a way out of the dilemma. So, for instance, the problem of sheer numbers of automobiles led to the development of freeways—and we all know parallels in the world of publication. When eventually the freeways become choked we shall find another solution, which may possibly involve the abolition of the automobile as we know it. So far as the menace of overpublication and its direful implication for the study of history are concerned, I have a few suggestions to make. The first two would probably be only palliative, and would require too much self-discipline for our current state of civilisation:

Firstly, scientists might perhaps learn something from creative artists, writers, musicians, painters and sculptors, many of whom are known actually to destroy, or at any rate to withhold from publication, works which do not measure up to their own self-imposed standards. Too many scientists are only too ready to add any kind of a notch to their bio-bibliography. We have yet to hear of a scientist refusing a Nobel Prize, as did Jean-Paul Sartre. We just don't seem to be built that way.

Secondly, we might suggest a self-imposed or society-imposed penalty on anyone who is forced to retract a published statement which was based on either insufficient learning, faulty or inadequate observation, or false reasoning. I would suggest at least a year's ban on further publication to allow him to put his house in order. For anyone who jumps the gun by publishing his correction or retraction as a footnote to the original paper the minimum sentence should be considerably longer.

Thirdly, a step that would probably transform the situation overnight would be if all academic appointment and promotion committees were to announce that rather than asking 'How many papers has the candidate published?' their policy normally is to ask instead the following three questions on this topic: (1) 'Has the candidate ever published anything of distinction, or even of considerable merit?'; (2) 'Has he ever, without real justification, published essentially the same work twice over?'; and (3) 'Has he ever put his name to any publication that is frankly second-rate?' I can almost see autobibliographies shrinking in size at the prospect.

It may be, though, that a simpler solution is already at hand. The standard technique of publication—that is, of making public, of communicating, one's ideas and conclusions—may very soon change out of all recognition. When the technique of printing was discovered it was first used, as indeed in some ways it still is, by anyone who sought a wider audience than could be reached by word of mouth. One does not have to go all the way with Professor Marshall McLuhan in his book *Understanding Media* to recognise that with the advent of electronic communication-systems the printed word is quite out of date so far as that original purpose is concerned. Why should we continue with this slow, ponderous and expensive technique of communication-in-isolation, when, with a little organisation, we could arrange for anyone to be in immediate visual and verbal contact with all those in the scientific community with whom he needs to communicate? The use of television-conferences should go far to restore the balance of interest in all four of those essential aims of academic life of which we spoke earlier. It will help to break the bonds of that out-of-date individualism, which is already over so far as practical science is concerned, but to which we still pay respect by including anywhere up to a dozen names in the authorship of a paper: authors often outnumbering their experimental animals by at least two to one, as a U.C.L.A. wit observed to me one day.

When the new media become the norm a scientist is unlikely to be prepared to expose himself to the critical gaze and comments of his peers unless he has first mastered the art of talking to an audience. The place for this training is the lecture-hall. Self-interest alone might lead faculty members actually to compete with one another for the privilege of giving lecture-courses to undergraduates in order to get some practice. Education will certainly benefit. As for Religion, if this is thought of in terms of integrity and commitment, then nothing picks out a phoney more accurately than good television, especially if it is two-way or multi-way television, with questions and comments coming from many sides. And lastly, if we think of Learning, he would be a foolish man who would enter into a nation-wide or world-wide television hook-up without being well briefed on all aspects of his subject, including its history. It is far more devastating to have one's ignorance exposed directly, before an audience, than to read about it in seclusion twelve months after one's offending article was published.

So, in conclusion, I see a big future for the History of Medical Science, and particularly for what I think is its most important branch, namely the history of ideas. Biographical and anecdotal history will never, perhaps, have more than an antiquarian interest, and that will be for the few to pursue professionally and for many to enjoy as recreation. It will not be bunk, to be sure, but it is unlikely ever to appeal to the practical man of science. But we medical scientists neglect the history of ideas at our peril. If we do, we shall have the doubtful honour of being judged by history, in our turn, as ingenious technocrats who were also ingenuous philistines, and guilty of intellectual treason. I submit, Mr President, that the challenge is with us here and now, and that it is high time we began to think seriously about it.

Perspectives in Biology and Medicine, 1966, vol. 10, pp. 44-55: Copyright 1966 by the University of Chicago.

9

COMMENTARIES ON KOESTLER
AND LEACH

At least four different facets of Koestler's intriguing personality are displayed in his latest book,[1] and it is well to be clear where he allows one to take over from another. He appears in the roles of (a) scientific journalist, (b) polemicist, (c) philosopher and creative thinker, and (d) prophet (somewhat paranoid). His scientific journalism is superb within the limits of the craft: it would seem incredible, if the book and its references were not there to prove it, that any one man should be capable of surveying an enormous range of biological science with such overall accuracy and insight. He writes with great force and skill, clearly aiming to be read not only by scientists but by a wide general public. It is well-known that this is a difficult art-form. It is also a crucially important one: bridging the gap that unquestionably exists, in this country, between the 'Two Cultures' will have to depend on writers like Koestler until such time as we have sense enough to reorganise our educational system.

Journalists, though, are inclined, in the interests of readability, to descend to the banal on occasion, and that is when inaccuracies can creep in. In the midst of an important discussion (p. 149) of the repeated development of organs of vision in the course of evolution, one suddenly winces at the following: 'Fishes, perhaps because they have more time on their fins, move the whole lens closer to the retina when

1. Koestler, A., *The Ghost In The Machine*, Hutchinson, London, 1967.

223

focussing on distant objects.' Is it because he was thrown by his own witticism that in the next sentence he goes on to make one of his relatively few scientific errors? In describing the more elegant and more complex method of focussing ('invented', probably, by mammal-like reptiles some 150 million years ago) that mammals including man use today, he has the lens flattening and thickening for near and distant objects respectively, instead of the reverse. It requires an effort to cause the lens to bulge when we look at near objects—as we most of us discover as we get older and find we can't do it as well as we once could.

The book is the third in a trilogy dealing with the nature of the scientific experience and the value of its methods and findings. In effect this one is a survey of the major features of biological evolution, and of the place and significance of man in the process. In the first few chapters we see Koestler the polemicist in fine debunking style. His blistering attack is once again levelled at the philosophy of behaviourism and what he calls 'ratomorphic psychology' (the 'rats-in-mazes' school). Behaviourism, where man is interpreted as though he were a rodent and rodents as though they were machines according to strict cartesian canons, has come under attack from many high-level scientists in recent years. But there is no doubt that its baleful influence, in which virtually all modern biologists were nurtured, is still very pervasive. Koestler has an amusing appendix 'On Not Flogging Dead Horses', where he describes the activities of a secret society devoted to the protection of the carcases of abandoned theories. Here is debunking in the best or worst traditions of the *genre*. However much one might approve the content (and perhaps it was time somebody said it forcefully and for general consumption), the method is surely very old-fashioned. Koestler has much to say on aggression. Debunking is how academics commonly satisfy their aggressive drives. It may be doubted whether any more good comes of it than comes of its physical counterpart. One wants to say 'Chuck it, chaps. There are better things to do with your intellectual gifts than thinking up devastating debating points.' Koestler may think that flogging dead horses may be worthwhile, but only, it seems, because he thinks they aren't quite dead yet. Surely we know enough about animal behaviour by now to know that flogging live ones doesn't get you very far either.

The principal positive feature of the book is his analysis of living things in terms of hierarchies of governing centres ('holons' as he calls them) within each organism. The concept leads him to explore the nature of the biological drive towards elaboration of more complex levels of organisation. This, he concludes, is one result of what he discerns as an integrative tendency at work within both the individual and the evolving group. The basic idea is not new. But Koestler's analysis and synthesis in terms of 'holons' is brilliant throughout. He achieves in this section a high level of argument. His admirable exposition has illuminating examples tumbling over themselves in support of his thesis. Old-fashioned mechanism, and its neo-Darwinian expression as 'chance plus natural selection' as the 'explanation' of the evolutionary process, is shown to be wholly inadequate to account for the world we know.

This analysis brings Koestler very close to Teilhard's theory of 'creative union' as the driving force of the evolutionary process. His only reference to Teilhard is in his sympathetic use of the concept of the 'noosphere', but he has clearly been influenced by the Jesuit's writings. Naturally he is not prepared to take the theory to its logical conclusions, because he insists on remaining within the secular-humanist camp. Secular humanists cannot, it seems, be optimistic about the long-term future of Man. And so we find Koestler the prophet of despair finally taking over from Koestler the creative philosopher. He adopts wholesale, and in quite uncritical fashion, the scientifically insupportable theories of the American clinical neurologist MacLean about the evolution of the human brain. He is thereby led to postulate, with MacLean, that Man's predicament derives from over-development of the 'neocortex' (or 'neopallium' as the jargon has it) of the cerebral hemispheres, with no adequate control over the phylogenetically older 'archipallium' and 'palaeopallium', which are taken to represent a kind of 'old Adam'. The account here adopted of the evolution of the mammalian and human brain, though correct in part, is so replete with anatomical misconceptions as to make the conclusions worthless. In an earlier book Koestler has correctly argued that the idea that scientific knowledge, once acquired, can never be lost, is demonstrably false. He and his mentor demonstrate the truth of this out of sheer ignorance of details of the science of comparative anatomy.

The author's answer to what is really the problem of 'original sin', is to urge the chemists to find a drug that will 'liberate' the neocortex from the constraints imposed by those parts of the cerebrum that were developed earlier. He gets into a remarkable tangle when discussing how his wonder-drug might be administered to all and sundry. He vaguely hopes that its use would spread, like that of alcohol, because of its pleasant effects. Temperance societies are not mentioned. This last section is not merely nonsense, it is dangerous nonsense. One hopes that in his next book he will have the courage and good sense to withdraw a pseudo-solution that has only the doubtful merit of keeping him within the ranks of those pessimistic humanists whose ideas are currently influential in many fields. Despair always was the worst sin, especially when drowned in alcohol or any other mind-relieving (mind-destroying?) drug.

The proper humanist answer to Koestler's dilemma is contained within his own analysis of hierarchies. He very rightly points out that man is adept at satisfying both his aggressive, self-assertive instincts and his altruistic drive towards self-transcendence, by creating a group (family, clan, political or religious group) and becoming aggressive on its behalf rather than his own. This trick has provided the basis for some of the cruellest acts of man, all the more cruel for being self-righteous. This fact lends credence, at a superficial level, to Koestler's theory of neurophysiological 'split-mindedness'. But the answer surely is clear: every community is a holon in Koestler's scheme. Modern communications-systems are making the whole world-community, in McLuhan's phrase, into that of a village. The roots of war and aggression lie in fear of 'the stranger'. When we no longer recognise strangers in this sense, but only fellow-men, there will be reason to hope for the future. But such a prospect leads straight into theology, and this is a road which Koestler and other secular humanists are not prepared to travel.

The Tablet, 1967, vol. 221, pp. 1222-4.

2. EDMUND LEACH: THOSE REITH LECTURES

'We must recognise that we are now responsible for the future. We cannot "leave it to Fate". But that does not mean that we must plan the future in detail: the most that we should try to do is to determine the general direction in which things move.... If we had all been educated so that values of toleration instead of values of aggressive competition were uppermost in our minds, we would take it for granted that long-term problems of nature conservancy were much more important than short-term problems of air defence; we would recognise at once the absurdity of building aircraft carriers and the utter barbarity of flogging schoolboys. Since we were not educated that way, we are still frightened and vindictive, but at least we can ensure that those who come after us are a little more civilised than ourselves.'

Thus the latest Reith lecturer towards the end of his series of broadcast talks, published in the six issues of *The Listener* from 16 November–21 December 1967.[2]

Never before has this annual series of lectures had such coverage in all sections of the Press. Not often has a university don—Edmund Leach is Provost of King's College, Cambridge, University Reader in Social Anthropology and a Vice-President of the Royal Anthropological Institute—caused such outbursts of hysteria in odd-looking (taken together) quarters: after all it isn't every week that you can hope to see Mrs Whitehouse cheek by jowl with Antony Flew in the correspondence-columns of *The Listener*—united in protest, at least, if from somewhat different standpoints. Leach made the headlines all right, as no doubt he had hoped to do. The newshounds (those experts in the art of *suppressio veri*) must have lain in wait by their radio-sets each Sunday evening, pencils at the ready to get down the most outrageous phrase they could find for the morning editions. With unerring accuracy, they all found the same ones—or were there press handouts, and if so who organised them?—the Provost himself, perhaps? Whatever the mechanisms, the Press presented Dr Leach to the public which didn't listen as a clown, a would-be shocker, a 'senior hipster', a madman with a gun blazing away at our hard-won British culture, almost the devil himself (or so it seemed to appear to some), enthroned in, of all places, the Provost's stall in King's chapel.

In Cambridge itself the publicity was treated with tolerant amusement. Not many dons, one suspects, listen to their colleagues' efforts even on Channel Three, let alone Four. Nobody imagines that the Monday morning newspapers give

2. Leach, Edmund, *A Runaway World? The Reith Lectures* 1967, BBC Publications, London, 1968.

a fair picture of anything so obviously controversial and news-worthy as these lectures were proving to be. (In conversation with one of the Fellows of King's, I referred to a *Times* corre-spondent who implied that he would start to take the Provost seriously when his College abandoned its position as a centre of privilege. My friend replied with a smile, 'He should come and see us any night of the week.' Hall is now a free-for-all in King's, run on a cafeteria system. Such straws in the wind are quickly seized by the kill-easy-die-hards that Dr Leach finds so evil, and therefore hard to tolerate.) So one had to wait for the printed text on Thursday to see whether the stories could really be true. The newspaper quotes were always to be found. But the qualifying clauses or sentences that usually clothed a statement that offended in the nude, had been judiciously omitted with the knowing wink that custom demands today even in quality newspapers. It was said in Cambridge that some of his more provocative statements had been censored by the BBC—so perhaps the Press was right, according to its lights, in trying to draw the lecturer's teeth before he started to bite really hard. For let there be no mistake, Leach was criticising all organs of the Establishment, and one suspects that the Press would come high on his list of things that we ought to im-prove.

Philip Toynbee seemed to think (*The Observer*, 24 December) that his teeth *had* been drawn by the time the sixth lecture was delivered. The piece started as follows: 'To read all six . . . is a disconcerting experience in a slightly different way, perhaps, than the one that he intended. For the first five lectures Dr Leach is like a cheeky schoolboy blowing raspberries and cocking snooks into every point of the compass. But in the sixth . . . just when the affronted elders are advancing on the impudent boy in a menacing circle, he suddenly holds up his hands and cries "Pax!" He doesn't explicitly retract what he has said earlier, but all the violently provocative statements are now reduced to conventional good sense.' Toynbee then quoted from each lecture in turn. Every phrase he used from the first five were those that the newshounds had picked for their Monday-morning stories. Not one of them, I submit, could be regarded as representative of the lecture as a whole. He quoted much more generously from the last one, and so his surprise is, perhaps, hardly surprising.

Other, more intemperate, commentators sounded off long before the end of the series. I don't want to suggest that everything depends on the *dénouement*, because I don't think there are any real inconsistencies involved. One may regret the 'shocking' phraseology at times, but all that went before is implicit in the last lecture, where Toynbee says he finds 'conventional good sense'. Leach would not like 'conventional'. Though he is no *revolutionary* (not to my mind at least) he is an *evolutionist* to his finger-tips. Both species are regarded as highly dangerous by the Establishment (academic, political, ecclesiastical, scientific), many of the members of which are so out of touch, and so committed in their subservience to the past, that they are unable to distinguish between the one and the other. The Second Vatican Council was faced with many of the same fundamental psychological problems that Leach was trying to get us all to face. Though he is reputed to be an anti-religious man, or even because he is, he should read this recent Church history. As a social anthropologist concerned with problems of kinship, ritual and taboo he would surely find much to fascinate him in an unusually well-documented record. He would find that Vatican II had important things to say about some of the problems that concern him, and that he rightly thinks ought to concern us all.

In particular he ought to study the writings of Newman and of Teilhard—the one an invisible *peritus* at the Council, the other a thinker whose brilliance shines ever more brightly in the light generated by it. Dr Leach is unquestionably a 'modern man' according to Teilhard's definition: 'What makes and classifies a "modern" man (and a whole host of our contemporaries is not yet "modern" in this sense) is having become capable of seeing in terms not of space and time alone, but also of duration, or—and it comes to the same thing—of biological space-time; and above all having become incapable of seeing anything otherwise—anything—*not even himself.*' Leach is such a man, who sees it to be vitally important that we realise, and grasp, our responsibilities for our 'runaway world'. There are many reasons for our current impotence and loss of control, some of them stemming from evolutionary theory itself, which has all too often suggested that individual effort, a sense of purpose, or a notion of 'direction' in the evolutionary process, are futile and absurd. These represent some of the early flounderings after man cast off his moorings from the safe, established, static or cyclical world of the past. Leach was contemptuous of those who cling excessively to the past. Teilhard, similarly and with some finesse, speaks of that host of contemporaries surrounding his 'modern' man as being, intellectually, still of the neolithic age. Angry reaction was inevitable. Coals of fire have been heaped upon the head of this year's Reith lecturer by a very odd assemblage of persons and groups, united only in aggression against an academic non-conformist who dared them to rethink their basic assumptions about, for instance, 'Who am I? What is Man? What is or should be our proper relation to a universe out of which we have been evolved and for which now, because we form the most complex part of it so far as we know, we must assume a creative responsibility?' The Establishment's current answers are either inadequate or just plain wrong. They are seen or 'sensed' to be wrong by the young, who are therefore in rebellion against their purblind elders. If the Establishment of Church, State, Universities, Political Parties, is unable or unwilling to respond to the challenge then they simply must go or be thrown out. Power corrupts, and the extent of the power that is now wielded by a very small proportion of the human race is colossal, and likely to prove disastrous if no action is taken.

The outburst of fury that greeted, in particular, the third lecture of the series (fittingly entitled 'Ourselves and Others') was a perfect example of the lecturer's thesis concerning the nature of aggression and the factors that predispose to it: fear of 'the other', fear of change, fear of anything that seems to threaten the orderliness of our inherited settled ways of living, or to threaten the modern meritocracy with its methods of selfish profiting from our structured social hierarchy. It was after this lecture that Leach was portrayed as a would-be destroyer of 'the family', an idea that produced an outburst of hysteria and hypocrisy in the Press. Are we to think, then, that Leach was being inconsistent when he said, in his fifth lecture, 'Education is not something primarily associated with school or technical college or university; it takes place mainly in the home . . . The sole purpose of education is to link things together, to establish communication, to make the child conscious that it is part of the family group . . . In the less sophisticated corners of the world, the kind of isolated loneliness which we consider normal—the emphasis on the uniqueness of the individual self separated from all others—is never cultivated at all. The child is born into a community which consists of whole classes of fathers and mothers, brothers and sisters, uncles and aunts, cousins and so on. In almost any situation there are half a dozen or so individuals who can act as stand-ins for any other. Moreover this is not just a temporary phase of early childhood: most people spend their whole lives surrounded and supported by kinsfolk.' This is in fact exactly the kind of 'family' that some of us remember, not so very long ago, in the small towns and villages of the North of England. It is being rapidly destroyed, not by increased mobility (which ought, together with other improvements in means of communication, to preserve and widen it) but by the extraordinary insistence of 'the planners' that what is best for a young married couple and their children is to isolate them (in the name of the sacred cow 'independence') in a 'convenient semi-detached' in the barren desert of a housing estate, or in a three-roomed flat on the fifteenth floor of some monstrous high-rise development. The only 'family' that Leach criticised was this nuclear family-unit, one of the effete end-products of the romantic movement, a unit isolated from all those ties of kinship on which so much of our emotional life depends, not only in childhood but also, because of its formative influence, throughout adult life too. I personally am grateful for the memories not only of my immediate family but also of all that larger family whose interconnections, between people of all ages and degrees (classified by means of a dozen different criteria), provided endless scope for conversation and friendship. If the choice is between the modern 'nuclear' family 'with its narrow privacy and tawdry secrets' (to use the phrase that got maximum publicity) and a kibbutz, or commune, or family as it was known to me as a boy, then give me the larger unit, and room to breathe, every time.

It wasn't only expressions long-hallowed by religious usage that were brought up for examination. In fact there was very little overt attack on religion except where formulations characteristic of a static world-picture appear to inhibit the development of a philosophy of process. Scientific positivism was also quietly but firmly put in its place. One of today's high-priests of scientific positivism is Sir Peter Medawar, whose book *The Art of the Soluble* has recently won high praise for its lucidity and for its scientific 'no nonsense' attitude. This is how its narrow ethos was dealt with in the first lecture: 'Again there is the evasion of responsibility: the glib doctrine that scientists are concerned with how things are, not with how they ought to be. What it boils down to is this. If you accept the argument that the only problems worth tackling are those which you have some chance of solving, then you must always assume, from the start, that everything proceeds according to orderly processes of cause and effect and probability. This applies whether you are dealing with a static situation or with a changing situation. So the very first basic assumption for any scientist is that the stuff he is studying is incapable of thinking for itself. It is not open to nature or any part of it to change the rules in the middle of the game. But that precisely is the difficulty. Man himself is a part of nature, and he *is* now capable of changing the rules.' Thus one Reith lecturer to another. As for another popular scientist, this is how the title of Desmond Morris's recent book was handled in the second lecture: 'Likewise Man is not just a naked ape, with a special shape of skull: he is a creature with a uniquely versatile technical facility for modifying his environment and communicating with other members of his species. . . . Of course Man is different, but he is not totally different. What we need to understand is not what Man is like "by himself" but what he is like in relation to all the rest. Where do we fit in?' Booksellers have been referring to this as 'the monkey Christmas': those who acquired *The Naked Ape* expecting to find justification (which they won't in the greater part of the book) for irresponsibility, would do well to study the Reith lectures for a lesson in the nature of human responsibility. Dr Leach uses all kinds of tricks to hold his audience, and the results certainly *seem* irresponsible at times. But underneath the squibs and rockets there is a serious and eminently worthwhile examination of the human predicament. Often enough he admits he doesn't know the answers. Often enough some possible answers he suggests may seem altogether inadequate, or unduly naïve. But they are never pig-headed. And at least he is asking the right questions, the important questions, and that is more than can be said for thousands of other gifted writers and broadcasters. How can answers ever be found until the questions are formulated and taken seriously?

It is not enough to analyse the present and to predict the future in terms of technical possibilities alone, because at the level of technology almost anything is seen today to be possible. What we need is a system of values. Mankind will no longer tolerate the imposition from above of any such system. It must be discovered from within, and that means hard work —and fast, if it is to be in time. Today we are conscious (the 'moderns' amongst us, at any rate) of living not in a cosmos but in a cosmogenesis. We need to know what this genesis means, so that we can act consciously in accordance with its meaning. One may have doubts about the Provost's choice of expression at times. One may have more serious doubts about his ability to help very much, except peripherally, in working out satisfactory answers to many of the problems he poses. But one must be grateful to him for making us think a good deal, and about important matters. He never did say, of course, how or whether 'we can determine the general direction in which things move'. Teilhard's 'law of complexity-consciousness' is likely to prove as important in this question as was Lyell's 'principle of uniformitarianism' in the development of nineteenth-century evolutionary theory. With Teilhard things seem to make sense again. With Leach there is only the possibility of a possibility that they may in time do so. But at least he closes no doors. And he opens a lot of windows to let some fresh air into our citadels of power and privilege.

The Month, 1968, vol. 225, pp. 104-10.

10

SCIENCE AND RELIGION:
A SUMMARY OF THE PROBLEMS
AND FUTURE PROSPECTS

Churchmen are constantly telling us that the days of conflict between science and religion are over. The fact that there ever was a conflict is much regretted, and is said to be due to a mistake about their respective fields of enquiry and methods of procedure. Hundreds of articles, sermons and books, written either by churchmen with a sympathetic (though usually uncomprehending) eye for science, or by scientists with a sympathetic (because usually committed) eye for religion, repeat *ad nauseam*, for instance, that science deals with things and with the how of the world, whereas religion deals with values and with the why of it all. These are really independent activities, it is said. Then, with one or two references to great men of science who were or are believers, it is concluded that peace and harmony have taken the place of a conflict that was logically unsound. A religious author may then bring in Einstein's oft-quoted remark that 'religion without science is blind, and science without religion is lame.' And everyone relaxes in the confident assurance that one of the greatest scientists acknowledged the need for religion—by everyone, of course, I mean those christians who alone seem to write and read this sort of thing.

Einstein's profound observation is no call to relaxation, indeed. But how often has it been used merely as an anodyne

236

or an antidepressant? 'Look,' our churchmen seem to say, 'we have no quarrel with you scientists. We recognise the importance of your work, and the significant achievements of the scientific revolution ['you'd better', might be the comment], and all we want is to live in peace. We promise not to attack you, so won't you join us in a non-aggression pact?' The overtures always seem to be one-way. Professional scientists mostly respond by politely ignoring the whole business. Non-aggression thereby ensues, of course, and religionists are lulled into thinking that all the things they very much want to believe about the compatibility between science and religion are true.

Is it not a strange and significant fact that whereas the religious side is everlastingly quoting examples of scientists who were also (or, more pointedly, became by conversion) men of faith, one never seems to hear professional scientists boasting of the same process the other way round? If a professional God-monger does some science he will be tolerated of course. But his science is likely to be counted as amateur or of the 'not particularly exacting' kind. Motives are often suspect, and conclusions, particularly if they tend to show any kind of real, 'existential' integration between science and religion, are dismissed as being biased or self-delusory or frankly dishonest. *Odium scientificum* can be as vicious as the older *odium theologicum*. Is it not on the whole better for both sides if cobblers stick to their lasts and merely overcome the temptation to throw them at one another's head?

The pretence, or delusion, that now that the nineteenth-century storms have finally abated, all is well between science and religion is, in my opinion, dangerous nonsense because, with its 'live and let live' attitude, it leads to complacency and apathy on both sides about the real activities of the other. The nonsense will inevitably result either in renewed conflict at some later date (and at a much increased intensity), or else in the elimination of one or other or both from the effective life-stream of civilisation. Putting the history of religion and the history of science into some kind of human perspective, it is not at all clear to me that the triumphalism of some modern scientists is any more justifiable (politically justifiable, I mean—triumphalism can surely never be morally justifiable) than that of the Church of yesterday. What I want to argue here is that, far from pretending that conflict is a thing of the past, and that all that we now need is polite exchange of information, we should realise that tension and conflict are inherent in this business, just as they are in any human activity really worth pursuing. Continual *engagement* (in all the varied meanings of that rich and noble word) is essential if progress in human understanding is to be made. Such engagement will naturally and normally be between exponents from each side—vigorous, healthy exponents, because there is no call for the mealy-mouthed in these matters, or for those who pretend to agree either because they don't understand or don't want to be thought ungenerous. Advances will not come if there is a typical common attitude towards 'victory' and 'defeat': 'to lose a round is not necessarily to lose the fight'—a cliché that sticks in the gullet and asks to be vomited forth with all those other aggressive clichés so beloved of tub-thumpers. Advances will rather come from an attitude of real enquiry and mutual assistance given in all humility, and with full recognition (provided exposition and actions warrant it) of the honesty and integrity of the others, and of the validity of their pursuit of truth.

Group-activity of this sort is surely the human activity *par excellence* of the future, because the day of the real polymath is long since over. No one can encompass more than a fraction of the scientific and religious fields of enquiry. And yet advances in mutual tolerance and respect will require not simply analysis in depth of particular areas of conflict and debate but, in addition to and prior to all that, the acknowledgement by each of the value of the underlying philosophy of the other. Such a 'feeling' is possible and meaningful only on the basis of experience. My argument is leading me to say that as well as encouraging conferences and committees to examine this and that, we should also encourage individuals to accept the necessity of conflict *within themselves*: to plan their lives consciously as 'workshops' for the refining and tempering (by crucible or forge, hammer and anvil as necessary) of whatever insights they might be able to achieve into the methods and techniques of both science *and* religion.

This is no call to a bed of roses. In our present culture it ought to be said, perhaps, that to call for hard work, sacrifice and pain, is no call to masochism either. The cross is a symbol not only of suffering and sacrifice but also, in anticipation of the resurrection, of joy and redemption. Every christian is called upon to take up the cross as Christ did, to experience pain and humiliation, suffering and sometimes despair perhaps. Comfort and complacency as the norm of living have no place in the christian religion, no more than they have in that other great 'religion', the pursuit of scientific knowledge and understanding. Great scientists normally have to suffer a good deal before any rewards start coming their way. And often enough, in the history of science, recognition has been posthumous or nearly so. But if every man has certainly to find his own way of salvation as a human being, there have been times in the past when a particular way has caught the imagination of large numbers of people.

Is it not time that christians, whether in formal religion or not, decided precisely to immerse themselves in the science/ religion conflict and sought personal integration through the cross of internal tensions that would inevitably arise? The object would be in no sense to baptise science or to secularise religion after the manner of so many would-be reformers, but rather to accept and live through the conflict with complete integrity in respect of both, faithful to the scientific method and faithful to religion. Both are phenomena that no one can afford to ignore if he is to give a meaningful account of this mysterious world-in-evolution of which he himself is both part and product.

If the complacent cleavage, referred to at the beginning of this article, is allowed to continue, it could well be that society will continue to reject and disdain a religion that fails to incorporate modern knowledge and continues to speak in a language that no longer communicates with the people. But in addition, if no more secure basis is discovered for science than it currently possesses, our age of science could come to an end just as surely as did those other equally powerful ages of the past. The signs of approaching demise, or self-destruction, in our technological civilisation, are to be seen currently in the widespread turning-away of the young from scientific studies, and in the increasing number of books by scientists and scientific journalists about the horrors in store for us if our 'runaway world' is allowed to run much further down the road opened up by the very success of science-in-isolation.

Once before Christianity rescued and preserved learning during a Dark Age. Einstein's observation on blindness and lameness should be taken absolutely seriously by men of both science and religion. Success in treatment of both these disabilities requires a wholeness of outlook currently possessed by comparatively few. As to which disability is the more prevalent, it seems to me that amongst my acquaintances the innumerates outnumber the illiterates. Despite the current power of science it may well be entering a period of extreme vulnerability, and no one who cares for mankind could view with equanimity its disappearance in a second Dark Age of civilisation. Science may have done comparatively little to support religion, but there would be no paradox if religion became the powerful supporter of science.

Frontier, 1968, vol. II, pp. 88–91.

ACKNOWLEDGMENTS

Where essays have previously appeared in print, the original reference is indicated at the end of the chapter concerned. Thanks are due to editors and publishers for permission to reprint them.

The author and publishers wish to thank the editors and publishers of the following journals for permission to reprint articles which originally appeared therein as:

The Month—'Man in Modern Science', see p. 25

'Evolution Today', see p. 200

'Those Reith Lectures', see p. 227

Blackfriars—'Teilhard de Chardin', see p. 43

'Teleology and the Anatomist', see p. 65

'The Significance of Teilhard de Chardin', see p. 124

The Listener—'Scientific Master Versus Pioneer. Bernard Towers on Medawar and Teilhard', see p. 89

Pax Romana Journal—'Optimism and Pessimism in Contemporary Culture', see p. 115

The Dublin Review—'Liberal and Vocational Education in the University', see p. 139

The Cambridge Review—'Religion and Biological Research', see p. 191

The Tablet—'Biology and the Electronic Village', see p. 223

Frontier—'The Vulnerability of Science', see p. 236

Expository Times—'Teilhard de Chardin', see p. 129

Acknowledgments

We are further indebted for permission to reprint copyright material as follows: for the essay 'Jung and Teilhard' from *Pilgrim of the Future: Teilhard de Chardin. Essays* edited by Neville Braybrooke (Seabury Press, U.S.A., 1964; Darton, Longman and Todd, England, 1966—originally published in *The Wind and The Rain* edited by Neville Braybrooke and published by Secker & Warburg, 1962); for the essay 'Medical Scientists and the View that History is Bunk', copyright 1966 by The University of Chicago; from *Science and Criticism: The Humanist Tradition in Contemporary Thought* by H. J. Muller and published by the Yale University Press; from *The Biology of the Spirit* by Edmond W. Sinnott, copyright © 1955 by Edmond W. Sinnott, reprinted by permission of the Viking Press, Inc.; from *Archives of Disease in Childhood*, 1967, Vol. 42, p. 224, by permission of the Editor; from *The Theory of Evolution* by John Maynard Smith and published by Penguin Books Ltd.; from *A Century of Darwin* edited by S. A. Barnett and published by Heinemann Educational Books Ltd.; from *Chemical Embryology* by J. Needham, *Man on His Nature*, Gifford Lectures 1937-38 by C. Sherrington and *My View of the World* by E. Shrödinger—all three published by the Cambridge University Press; from *General Biology and Philosophy of Organism* by R. S. Lillie and published by The University of Chicago Press copyright 1945; from *Medicine in the 1860's: Proceedings of the Sixth British Congress on the History of Medicine*, 1967, edited by F. N. L. Poynter, London Royal Historical Medical Library, 1968.

The article 'Life Before Birth', copyright The Pierre Teilhard de Chardin Association of Great Britain and Ireland 1967, has been previously published in *Evolution, Marxism and Christianity* by the Garnstone Press.

INDEX

INDEX

247

Index

Index

Index

Index

Index

The author, a biologist of international renown, considers that we live in a fragmented society. These vital and immensely readable essays are an attempt to look at life in the round. He refuses to follow one stream of culture to the exclusion of others and insists on exploring every aspect that seems to be valid, significant and true in his search for an answer to the question: Who am I and what, if anything, am I here for? Other questions he is asking are:

If it be true, as some seem to think, that people are only 'naked apes', has an ape (or any other feature of 'nature') any relevance or significance, or is everything really just a mess? Is death—my own death, the death of relations and friends, the deaths of people on motorways, in Vietnam, or Biafra, or in earthquakes—anything more than a mark of ultimate absurdity in a manifestly absurd life? Is it possible for a practising biological scientist and university teacher to preserve his intellectual integrity while at the same time following religious teaching of Christianity and in particular of Roman Catholicism?

The first essay is called *Where Three Roads Meet.* These roads are science, religion and philosophy. He maintains that discussion of the interrelationship of these subjects has never been more vital for contemporary society. In view of the quite extraordinary physical and biological powers that rest with us today, neglect of the larger question could, in the quite near future, lead to the destruction of society and civilisation.

He points out that tension is bound to exist between science, philosophy and religion, and that in academic circles in this age of specialisation any attempt to build bridges between them is frowned upon. Bernard Towers shows how a